New Directions 15

NEW DIRECTIONS 15

*An anthology of new directions
in prose and poetry*

International issue

MERIDIAN BOOKS   *New York 1955*

Dedicated to James Agee, 1909–1955

Published by New Directions and Meridian Books
Copyright 1955 by New Directions
Library of Congress Catalog Card Number: 55–10072

Contents

New Directions 15

EDITORS' NOTE

This is the fifteenth in a series of anthologies which began to appear in 1936. It is the first in a new format which we hope old friends will welcome as easier to handle and less costly to own. We leave the spaciousness of the old 6 x 9 page with regret—it gave us plenty of room in which to make the mistakes to which we were, by principle, committed—but we leave it with the promise that if our readers will support the new venture as indulgently as they did the old one we shall try to make up in frequency—and regularity—for what may be lost in bulk.

Specifically, we would welcome comment on the suggestion that *New Directions* might alternate between international numbers, such as this one, and issues devoted to the new, the young, and the different in our own country—with perhaps, where the interest challenges and our strength permits, an occasional extra volume devoted to a country in whose culture great things may be stirring, or to a special field in which new trends command fresh scrutiny.

For new readers—and we hope that our kind hosts, Meridian Books, will introduce us to many of them—some past history may not be out of order. The first *New Directions in Prose & Poetry* appeared in 1936. It contained selections of

Pound and Stein, of Cummings and Cocteau, of Stevens and Miss Moore and Dr. Williams and a dozen others who were all in those distant days more or less unacceptable to the older professors of literature in the colleges. It had a brash, unlovely red and yellow cover, and was printed in a small Vermont town by a printer who also did the *Harvard Advocate*. It was sold to a largely uninterested book trade in moments snatched from his schoolwork by a Harvard sophomore more notable for energy than sense. And all this because the said sophomore—unhumble, unruly and (by European standards at least) uneducated—had (1) a lot of vim to burn up and a compulsion to do it by shocking the tastes of the sedate and perplexed parents to whom fate had issued such a monster, and (2) by chance been exposed in prep school to a great teacher (Dudley Fitts) who had carried him in one furious bound from Scott and Dickens to Joyce and Eliot, and later, in a rebellious *wanderjahr,* to the great fructifying iconoclast of our century, Ezra Pound, who told him that if "he wanted to be of some use" he had better go back home and "do something" about Professor Hillyer (who would not let the name Eliot be uttered in his Harvard classes) and Dr. Canby (who averred there was no character development in *Ulysses*) and about getting Bill Williams into print.

So much has the climate changed—for the better—in twenty years, it may now seem hard to believe that there was a moment in our literary history when the most essentially American of our writers could not find a publisher for his *White Mule,* but that was the fact. Perhaps it was the Depression with its drift toward pro-Marxist content; perhaps it was only a natural lull after the lively drive of *The Little Review,* Jolas' *transition* and Kirstein's *Hound & Horn.*

In any case, there was a place for *New Directions* and it filled it in a bumbling, irritating, never-satisfying-everybody-or-anybody sort of way. Not to satisfy everybody was, of course, the cardinal principle: both for the anthology and for the publishing imprint that grew up along with it. The theory was simply this: literature, a whole culture in fact, goes dead when there is no experiment, no reaching out, no counterattack on accepted values. Even if the experiment is a failure, it must exist as a force and be given a showing place. And not completely to satisfy anybody was also intentional. There was to be no one cult and no one canon. From the first, space was saved for writers whose work the editor personally did not like but which was vouched for by people whose judgment he respected. *Spearhead,* the anthology which summarizes the first ten years of the *New Directions* anthologies, tells the story: Schwartz and Patchen, whose adherents generally despise each other's taste, are side by side; the diffuse Henry Miller keeps company with the strict John Berryman, and Tennessee Williams makes his poetry out of the emotions, while John Wheelwright made his out of the mind.

Beyond this catholicity, there was another rule; not to meddle with what others were already doing well enough. The best writing in conventional and traditional forms was readily getting published in a number of excellent magazines. So that was not our concern: an omission which persistently troubled the critics who would industriously belabor the experimentalists on grounds which were never claimed for them. And of course there were every year two or three intelligent essays which conclusively proved that the revolution of forms was over, that the advance guard were now the after-stragglers, and that we were luring the deluded into a house of ghosts. But, ghosts or not, an increasing number of readers has seemed to want to get into the house . . . and we mean to keep a roof over it for as long as we can honesty feel that we are keeping the door unlatched and the windows unshuttered.

Particularly we want the door to be open in the next years for writers of other lands and especially those of Asia. As the politicians of the West, with their "ecclesiastical foxiness," continue to demonstrate an almost total incomprehension of reality and an inability to deal with the forces their wrong attitudes have engendered, it becomes more than ever the duty, and beyond that the last hope in despair, of writers and editors, and of readers who look to poets rather than public relations spellbinders for their truth, to establish and maintain through arts and letters a common meeting ground for intercultural understanding and future living together on this planet.

Making such an exchange meaningful is not easy. The "world literature" of which Goethe dreamed is still a long way off. Most of the Asian writers represented in this collection have had European or European-influenced educations. It has been impossible to convince a Sanscrit-scholar friend in Madras that what Cummings writes is poetry; and to some highly-educated Arabs many of the accepted forms of Western writing are still alien. It is a crime that so few of the humanities courses in American colleges even sample the great books of the Eastern cultures. And something should be done about sending as many American writers and artists as salesmen and technicians to the "undeveloped" countries—to learn instead of teach. More of us here should realize that *we* need the spiritual development—the know-how of how to *live*—which the Asiatics can bring us quite as much as they need our industrial and agricultural techniques.

Only a mass effort to change thinking—a great wave of revulsion against smugness and belief in the efficacy of force —can accomplish the major objectives. But we think that we can at least make these *New Directions* volumes a helpful symbol by welcoming foreign writers to our pages and by printing various kinds of American writing which may help convince our would-be friends abroad that our cultural channels have not become as badly clogged up as the political.

J.L.
R.M.M.

POSTHUMOUS

KHUSHWANT SINGH

I am in bed with fever. It is not serious. In fact, it is not serious at all, as I have been left alone to look after myself. I wonder what would happen if the temperature suddenly shot up. Perhaps I would die. That would be really hard on my friends. I have so many and am so popular. I wonder what the papers would have to say about it. They couldn't just ignore me. Perhaps the *Tribune* would mention it on its front page with a small photograph. The headline would read "Sardār Khushwant Singh Dead"—and then in somewhat smaller print:

"*We regret to announce the sudden death of Sardār Khushwant Singh at 6 p.m. last evening. He leaves behind a young widow, two infant children and a large number of friends and admirers to mourn his loss. It will be recalled that the Sardār came to settle in Lahore some five years ago from his home town, Delhi. Within these years he rose to a position of eminence in the Bar and in politics. His loss will be mourned generally throughout the Province.*

"*Amongst those who called at the late Sardār's residence were the P.A. to the Prime Minister, the P.A. to the Chief Justice, several Ministers and Judges of the High Court.*

13

"In a statement to the press, the Hon'ble the Chief Justice said: 'I feel that the Punjab is poorer by the passing away of this man. The cruel hand of death has cut short the promise of a brilliant career.'"

At the bottom of the page would be an announcement:

"The funeral will take place at 10 a.m. today."

I feel very sorry for myself and for all my friends. With difficulty I check the tears which want to express sorrow at my own death. But I also feel elated and want people to mourn me. So I decide to die—just for the fun of it as it were. In the evening, giving enough time for the press to hear of my death, I give up the ghost. Having emerged from my corpse, I come down and sit on the cool marble steps at the entrance to wallow in posthumous glory.

In the morning I get the paper before my wife. There is no chance of a squabble over the newspaper as I am downstairs already, and in any case my wife is busy puttering around my corpse. The *Tribune* lets me down. At the bottom of page 3, column 1, I find myself inserted in little brackets of obituary notices of retired civil servants—and that is all. I feel annoyed. It must be that blighter Shafi, Special Representative. He never liked me. But I couldn't imagine he would be so mean as to deny me a little importance when I was dead. However, he couldn't keep the wave of sorrow which would run over the Province from trickling into his paper. My friends would see to that.

Near the High Court the paper is delivered fairly early. In the house of my lawyer friend Qādir it is deposited well before dawn. It isn't that the Qādirs are early risers. As a matter of fact, hardly anyone stirs in the house before 9 A.M. But Qādir is a great one for principles and he insists that the paper must be available early in the morning even if it is not looked at.

As usual, the Qādirs were in bed at 9 A.M. He had worked very late at night. She believed in sleep anyhow. The paper was brought in on a tray along with a tumbler of hot water with a dash of lime juice. Qādir sipped the hot water between intervals of cigarette smoking. He had to do this to make his bowels work. He only glanced at the headlines in bed. The real reading was done when the cigarette and lime had had their effect. The knowledge of how fate had treated me had to await the lavatory.

In due course Qādir ambled into the bathroom with the paper in one hand and a cigarette perched on his lower lip. Comfortably seated, he began to scan it thoroughly and his eye fell on news of lesser import. When he got to page 3, column 1, he stopped smoking for a moment, a very brief moment. Should he get up and shout to his wife? No, he decided, that would be an unnecessary demonstration. Qādir was a rationalist. He had become more of one since he married a woman who was a bundle of emotions and explosions. The poor fellow was dead and nothing could be done about it. He knew that his wife would burst out crying when he told her. That was all the more reason that he should be matter-of-fact about it—just as if he was going to tell her of a case he had lost.

Qādir knew his wife well. He told her with an air of casualness, and she burst out crying. Her ten-year-old daughter came running into the room. She eyed her mother for a little while and then joined her in the wailing. Qādir decided to be severe.

"What are you making all this noise for?" he said sternly. "Do you think it will bring him back to life?"

His wife knew that it was no use arguing with him. He always won the arguments.

"I think we should go to their house at once. His wife must be feeling wretched," she said.

Qādir shrugged his shoulders.

"I am afraid I can't manage it. Much as I would like to condole with his wife—or rather widow—my duty to my clients comes first. I have to be at the tribunal in half an hour."

Qādir was at the tribunal all day and his family stopped at home.

Not far from the city's big park lives another friend, Khosla. He and his family, consisting of a wife three sons and a daughter, reside in this upper-class residential area. He is a judge and very high up in the bureaucracy.

Khosla is an early riser. He has to rise early because that is the only time he has to himself. During the day he has to work in the Courts. In the evenings he plays tennis—and then he has to spend some time with the children and fussing with his wife. He has a large number of visitors, as he is very popular and enjoys popularity. But Khosla is ambitious. As a lad he had fancied himself as a clever boy. In his early youth his hair had begun to fall off and had uncovered a large bald forehead. Khosla had looked upon it as nature's confirmation of his opinion about himself. Perhaps he was a genius. The more he gazed upon his large head in the mirror, the more he became convinced that fate had marked for him an extraordinary career. So he worked harder. He won scholarships and rounded off his academic career by topping the list in the Civil Service examination. He had justified the confidence he had in himself by winning laurels in the stiffest competitive examination in the country. For some years he lived the life of a contented bureaucrat. In fact, he assured himself that he was what people called "a success in life."

After some years this contentment had vanished. Every time he brushed the little tuft at the back of his head and ran his hands across his vast forehead he became conscious of unrealised expectations. There were hundreds of senior civil servants like him. All were considered successes in life. The Civil Service was obviously not enough. He would work—he would write—he knew he could write. There it was written in the size of his head. So Khosla took to writing. In order to write well he took to reading. He amassed a large library and regularly spent some hours in it before going to work.

This morning Khosla happened to be in a mood to write. He made himself a cup of tea and settled in a comfortable armchair by the electric radiator. He stuck the pencil in his mouth and meditated. He couldn't think of what to write. He decided to write his diary. He had spent the previous day listening to an important case. It was likely to go on for some days. The courtroom had been packed and everyone had been looking at him—that seemed a good enough subject. So he started to write.

Khosla was disturbed by the knock of the bearer bringing in the paper. He opened the news-sheet to read the truths of mundane existence.

Khosla was more interested in social affairs, births, marriages and deaths, than events of national or international import. He turned to page 3, column 1. His eye caught the announcement and he straightened up.

He just tapped his notebook with his pencil, and after a wake-up cough informed his wife of the news. She just yawned and opened her large dreamy eyes wide.

"I suppose you will close the High Court today?" she said.

"I am afraid the High Court doesn't close at just any excuse. I'll have to go. If I have any time I'll drop in on the way—or we can call on Sunday."

The Khoslas did not come. Nor did many others for whose sorrow at my demise I had already felt sorrowful.

At 10 o'clock a little crowd had collected in front of the open space beneath my flat. It consisted mainly of people I did not expect to see. There were some lawyers in their court dress, and a number of sightseers who wanted to find out what was happening. Two friends of mine also turned up, but they stood apart from the crowd. One was a tall, slim man who looked like an artist. With one hand he kept his cigarette in place, the other he constantly employed in pushing his long hair off his forehead. He was a writer. He did not believe in attending funerals. But one had to hang around for a little while as a sort of social obligation. It was distasteful to him. There was something infectious about a corpse—so he smoked incessantly and made a cigarette smoke-screen between himself and the rest of the world.

The other friend was a Communist, a short, slight man with wavy hair and a hawkish expression. His frame and expression belied the volcano which they camouflaged. His approach to everything was coldly Marxist and sentiment found no place in it. Deaths were unimportant events. It was the cause that mattered. He consulted the writer in a polite whisper.

"How far are you going?"

"I plan dropping off at the coffeehouse," answered the other. "Are you going the whole way?"

"No ruddy fear," said the Communist emphatically. "Actually I had to be at a meeting at ten, and I was planning to be free of this by 9:30—but you know our people haven't the foggiest idea about time. I'll get along to the Party office now and then meet you at the coffeehouse at 11:30. Incidentally if you get an opportunity, just ask the hearse driver if he is a member of the Tongāwālā Union. Cheers."

A little later a hearse, drawn by a bony brown horse arrived and pulled up in front of my doorstep. The horse and his master were completely oblivious of the solemnity of the occasion. The driver sat placidly chewing his betelnut and eyeing the assembly. He was wondering whether this was the type likely to produce a tip. The beast straightaway started to piddle and the crowd scattered to avoid the spray which rebounded off the brick floor.

The crowd did not have to wait very long. My corpse was brought down all tied up in white linen and placed inside the hearse. A few flowers were ceremoniously placed on me. The procession was ready to start.

Before we moved another friend turned up on his bicycle. He was somewhat dark and flabby. He carried several books on the carrier and had the appearance of a scholarly serious-minded professor. As soon as he saw the loaded hearse, he dismounted. He had great respect for the dead and was particular to express it. He put his bicycle in the hall, chained it, and joined the crowd. When my wife came down to bid her last farewell he was visibly moved. From his pocket he produced a little book and thoughtfully turned over its pages. Then he slipped through the people towards my wife. With tears in his eyes he handed the book to her.

"I've brought you a copy of the *Gita*. It will give you great comfort."

Overcome with emotion, he hurriedly slipped back to wipe the tears which had crept into his eyes.

"This," he said to himself with a sigh, "is the end of human existence. This is the truth."

He was fond of thinking in platitudes—but to him all platitudes were profound and had the freshness and vigor of original thought.

"Like bubbles," he said to himself, "human life is as momentary as a bubble."

But one didn't just die and disappear. Matter could not immaterialise—it could only change its form. The *Gita* put it so beautifully—

"Like a man casts off old garments to put on new ones . . . So does the soul, etc., etc."

The professor was lost in contemplation. He wondered what new garments his dead friend had donned.

His thoughts were disturbed by a movement between his legs. A little pup came round the professor's legs licking his trousers and looking up at him. The professor was a kind man. He involuntarily bent down and patted the little dog, allowing him to lick his hands.

The professor's mind wandered—he felt uneasy. He looked at the corpse and then at the fluffy little dog at his feet, who after all was part of God's creation.

"Like a man casts off old garments to put on new ones . . . So does the soul . . ."

No, no, he said to himself. He shouldn't allow such uncharitable thoughts to cross his mind. But he couldn't check his mind. It wasn't impossible. The *Gita* said so, too. And he bent down again and patted the pup with more tenderness and fellow feeling.

The procession was on the move. I was in front, uncomfortably laid within the glass hearse, with half a dozen people walking behind. It went down toward the river.

By the time it had passed the main street, I found myself in solitude. Some of the lawyers had left at the High Court. My author friend had branched off to the coffeehouse, still smoking. At the local college, the professor gave me a last longing, lingering look and sped up the slope to his classroom. The remaining six or seven disappeared into the District Courts.

I began to feel a little small. Lesser men than myself had had larger crowds. Even a dead pauper carried on a municipal wheelbarrow got two sweepers to cart him off. I had only one human being, the driver, and even he seemed to be oblivious of the enormity of the soul whose decayed mansion he was transporting on its last voyage. As for the horse, he was positively rude.

The route to the cremation ground is marked with an infinite variety of offensive smells. The climax is reached when one has to branch off the main road toward the crematorium along a narrow path which runs beside the city's one and only sewer. It is a stream of dull, black fluid with bubbles bursting on its surface all the time.

Fortunately for me, I was given some time to ruminate over my miscalculated posthumous importance. The driver pulled up under a large *peepul* tree near where the road turns off to the cremation ground. Under this *peepul* tree is a tonga stand and a water trough for horses to drink out of. The horse made for the water and the driver clambered off his perch to ask the tonga drivers for a light for his cigarette.

The tonga drivers gathered round the hearse and peered in from all sides.

"Must be some one rich," said one. "But there is no one with him," queried another. "I suppose this is another English custom—no one to go with funerals."

By now I was thoroughly fed-up. There were three ways open to me. One was to take the route to the cremation ground and, like the others that went there, give myself up to scorching flames, perhaps to be born again into a better world, but probably to be extinguished into nothingness. There was another road which forked off to the right towards the city. There lived harlots and other people of ill-repute.

They drank and gambled and fornicated. Theirs was a world of sensation and they crammed their lives with all the varieties which the senses were capable of registering. The third one was to take the way back. It was difficult to make up one's mind. In situations like these the toss of a coin frequently helps. So I decided to toss the coin; heads and I hazard the world beyond; tails and I go to join the throng of sensation seekers in the city; if it is neither heads nor tails and the coin stands on its edge, I retrace my steps to a humdrum existence bereft of the spirit of adventure and denuded of the lust for living.

THE PASSION OF CÉSAR VALLEJO

H. R. HAYS

Peru's greatest modern poet, César Vallejo, was born in 1893 in Santiago de Chuco, a tiny provincial capital in the northern sierras, six hours from the port of Trujillo. The inhabitants of the town retain much of the Indian's closeness to the soil; houses are primitive adobe shells, without sanitary conveniences, and sparsely furnished; chickens and guinea pigs swarm in the kitchen and patio. (Guinea pigs have been a delicacy since Inca times). Whole clans live together, uncles, aunts, cousins, grandparents, swarms of children, in patriarchal unity. While the cholos speak Spanish, they generally have some knowledge of Quecha and can sing the Indian dance songs. Nevertheless, since they also share in the traditions which accompany Spanish blood, they are capable of making sacrifices so that members of the family can achieve a higher education. Their white blood breaks down the barrier which a pure Indian feels, the suspicion and distrust of civilization which centuries of exploitation have inculcated. Vallejo, the bronze-skinned cholo, united in himself the two elements in Peruvian life.

Vallejo's brother, Manuel, worked in the office of a tungsten mine. The exploitation of the Indian laborers by both

North American and middle-class Peruvian officials, which he observed, became the basis for *Tungsteno,* the novel which César wrote many years later. On nearby haciendas, Indians labored for little or no pay, subsisting on minimal company rations, in filthy one-room barracks. The bitter facts of the Peruvian social situation were indelibly printed on Vallejo's mind from earliest childhood.

That his childhood was happy, we can gather from the nostalgia with which he wrote of his home and family. There were eight other children—their names are recorded in his poems in tender tribute. A journalist, Izquierdo Rios, visited his sisters in Santiago de Chuco in 1947. They had retained no letters or mementos of the poet. Simple folk, they had no understanding of the importance of his work. An older brother, Nestor, a lawyer in Trujillo, provided me with a few anecdotes. Apparently relatives and friends remembered him as a slightly crazy young man. The town has finally named the street of his birth after him, but it is obvious that provincial taste is still far from catching up with his poetry.

Vallejo's father was "governor" of the town for many years and apparently highly respected. His mother, whose influence was of the greatest importance, died in 1918; in one of his last poems he addresses her as if she were still alive, and creates an image of her which abounds in gentleness and humility.

Vallejo attended the Colegio Nacional de Huamachuco in a neighboring province. He obtained his bachelor's degree in letters at the University of Trujillo in 1916, writing his thesis on "Romanticism in Castillian Poetry."

César's years as a student in Trujillo were extremely important. They coincided with the beginning of a new social consciousness which awoke after the First World War. The University Reform movement was initiated in Argentina in 1914 and rapidly took root all over Latin America. At first it was essentially a protest against the medieval curriculum inherited from Spain; an attempt to bring modern science and contemporary points of view into the Spanish-American university. Later, the movement took on a social color when many of its leaders became interested in revolutionary activity which, for the first time, united Latin-American intellectuals with the cause of the people.

During the time that Vallejo attended the University, there was a group of young bohemians who later became important in the socio-cultural history of Peru. Haya de la Torre, leader of the Reform movement, became the founder of the radical Aprista Party (the Alianza Popular Revolucionaria de America) which, as a result of the unsuccessful revolution of October 3, 1948, was outlawed and persecuted. Alcides Spelucín, poet and Aprista leader, became professor in the University of San Marcos, and Antenor Orrego, who wrote the introduction to Vallejo's first book of verse, was also destined to become a leading member of Apra, and rector of the University of Trujillo. The group also included the painter, Alfonso Sanchez Urteaga and the journalist, José Eulogio Garrido. In the sleepy, white-washed, colonial city of Trujillo this group of romantic young men drank and discussed, read and recited loudly as they paced up and down the beaches; they visited little villages populated by Indians, descendants of those who built the mighty pre-Incan city of Chan-Chan, on the outskirts of Trujillo. In village restaurants they ate roast kid and drank chicha (maize beer). Their favorite poets were Ruben Darío, Verlaine, Amado Nervo, Paul Fort, Samain, Maeterlinck and Walt Whitman.

The novelist Ciro Alegría paints, from the point of view of a schoolchild, a picture of the poet, then teaching in the Colegio Nacional de San Juan. The teacher's long black hair puzzled the child. He was told Vallejo wore his hair long because he was a poet. Alegría describes him as thin, sallow, almost hieratical looking, like a tree bare of leaves.

His skin was dark and, from his photographs one can see the monumental forehead, the craglike brows, the high, protruding Indian cheekbones. As a teacher, he combined great tenderness with brusqueness and melancholy. He was often late to school (doubtless after late sessions with his friends), and was once reprimanded by the principal. He also failed to make the children march in well-drilled formation on Independence Day. But he used to say to his students, "Come, let's talk," and encouraged them to tell stories and observe the details of their environment. Alegría came to be much impressed by his eccentric schoolmaster. The latter had already published in periodicals some of the poems which were to be collected in *Los heraldos negros* (Black Harbingers). The public was sharply divided over his work. Alegría, whose curiosity was piqued, tried to read his teacher's poems himself. Since Ciro was only eight, he did not understand them but was left with a vague sense of excitement and hero worship. Orrego says that many of the university professors, whose literary taste stopped short with the work of Alexandre Dumas, attacked Vallejo with senile violence.

Finally, Vallejo left for Lima, where he continued leading a bohemian life. He taught for a time in the Colegio de Guadaloupe but his intense and eccentric character never adapted itself to academic life.

According to Luis Alberto Sanchez, Vallejo was discovered as a poet by Valdelomar and about this time he began a correspondence with the Arequipa poet, Percy Gibson. He continued his studies in philosophy and letters at the University of San Marcos. Sanchez says that he was Vallejo's only friend among the professors. The poet published his first volume which was received with critical incomprehension, and began to think, as did most young artists of South America in those days, of widening his horizon by visiting Europe.

Vallejo's biography has not been written, and until it is, much of his life remains unrecorded. It is evident, however, that he made some literary friends in Lima, that he drank and discussed, and, in imitation of Parisian fin-de-siècle bohemia, experimented with drugs. An event which took place in 1920, has been much discussed, and was undoubtedly a turning point in his life. He returned to Santiago de Chuco, on what he may have considered a farewell visit before leaving the country, on the 28th of July, Independence Day. The local prefect, who was a friend of Vallejo's was absent, and the substitute prefect was a military man from another province, who brought some of his own gendarmes with him; the local

gendarmes clashed with the outsiders, and Don Antonio
Ciudad, a friend of Vallejo's, was killed in the fracas. A ware-
house was set on fire by Ciudad's friends in reprisal. Vallejo
was implicated in the affair, and as a result spent three months
in jail where he wrote some of the poems published in *Trilce*
and the long story *Fabla salvaje* (Savage Fable). According to
his brother, Nestor, and accounts written by his friends, the
artists and intellectuals of Peru agitated for his release, and he
was eventually cleared and set free. The episode has been described as political persecution. Vallejo was, no doubt, a political radical; Nestor maintains that the affair was the result
of local pettiness and personal antagonisms, and that Vallejo,
already a figure of some prominence, was the victim of vindic-
tive jealousy. The experience was a tragic one for the poet,
and intensified his disorientation from the provincial environment. Vallejo went abroad in May 1923.

How he accumulated the fare and how he managed when
he first set foot in Paris—according to Mori, with no money
and a handbook of French in ten easy lessons—is a mystery.
Juan Larrea, writing of this epoch in the poet's life, says,
". . . His vein of poetry, whose wealth had diminished seriously since his arrival in Europe, moved toward the twilight,
toward an extinction which seemed more and more unavoidable. . . . The years '23, '24, '25, winters stiff with cold, in-
termittent lodging, without clothes to cover him. The years
'26, '27, '28, with an interior crisis. . . ."

Ernesto Mori says he lived at times in the studio of a sculptor and that he had a girl named Henriette who worked and
helped support him. Their diet was potatoes and when they
had cheese as well, they considered it a fiesta. When Vallejo
had no lodgings, he slept in parks and in the Paris Metro. He
developed elaborate theories: he avoided sitting down in order to prevent his clothes from wearing out, and he would
explain just how to step out of the Metro to spare his shoes.
He told Mori that many times he stood on bridges considering suicide; one is aware of the death-fixation in his poems.

In the years 1925 and 1926, he had a minor scholarship
from Spain. Raul Porras Barrenechea, also writing of this pe-

riod, says, "Arriving in Europe, Vallejo lived the bohemian life of a South American expatriate. He saw Paris in the galleries of the Louvre and in the golden light of the sun over the cupola of the Sacré Coeur; he wandered through cafés and hotels . . . he lived in Montparnasse between the Dôme and the Rotonde and, across from the Comédie Française, the Café de la Regencie reflected his Indian cheekbones, his Beethoven forehead, in its mirrors. . . ."

In January, 1929, he married a French girl, Georgette, who from the window of her house facing Vallejo's hotel, had watched him, fascinated, without his knowing it. Shortly after their marriage, her mother died, and on the proceeds from the latter's store, they travelled extensively in European cities. Vallejo appears to have had commissions from Madrid newspapers. They were very unhappily married.

Back in France, on the 28th of December, 1931, the Vallejos were arrested and expelled from France because of radical activity. Then, for the first time, Vallejo lived in Spain. This country became the poet's obsession and, as Larrea suggests, his mother fixation was replaced by a fixation on Spain. In Madrid, he wrote his novel, *Tungsteno*. Shortly afterward he published a collection of articles, *Russia, 1931*. The Madrid papers for which he wrote, *Ahora*, *Estampa* and *La voz* rejected fifteen articles on Russia because, even though he needed the money, he refused to cut certain passages.

He wrote a play, *Mamper*, which he subsequently destroyed; it was followed by a social drama, *Lockout*. While in Spain, he became friendly with Alberti, Salinas, Larrea, and García Lorca. His closest Peruvian friends were Xavier Abril and Juan Luis Vasquez. *Trilce* had already been published in Spain in 1930 with a preface by José Bergamin. In 1932, the Chautemps government granted him and his wife permission to return to France. The round of hotels commenced again. Sick and poverty-stricken, he went on writing for the theater without success. At this time he collected notes, articles and pages of a diary, *El arte y la revolución* (*Art and Revolution*) and *Contra el secreto profesional* (*Against the Professional Secret*).

In July 1937 he went to Spain, in the midst of the war, to attend the Congress of Revolutionary Writers. The Spanish war moved Vallejo profoundly and awakened his poetic impulse which had lain dormant for more than ten years. He returned to Paris at the end of the year and began writing *Poemas humanos*, the volume which contains his finest work. In this last year of his life, he wrote continuously, at a feverish pitch. Luis Valcárcel, who saw a good deal of him when he was working on the Peruvian Pavillion for the Paris Exposition of 1937, for which Vallejo did some translating, says they talked of starting a magazine together in Lima. In all his expatriate years, Vallejo had never ceased to be utterly Peruvian.

That Vallejo's thoughts were turning homeward is borne out by his last work, completed just before he died, *La piedra cansada* (*The Tired Stone*), a poetic drama on an Incan theme. He reserved his passage home; months passed and he did not leave. A friend told Valcárel, who was awaiting him in Peru, that Vallejo's wife refused to come.

Early in 1938, Vallejo was attacked by a fever and moved to a hospital where various tests and analyses were made without results. For months his temperature hovered between 104 and 106 degrees. He died on April 15 in the Clinico Arago, with no diagnosis having been established. As he had prophesied in one of his poems, he died "in a shower of rain, In Paris, on Thursday," in the larger sense struck down by hunger and by Spain's agony.

POEMS BY CÉSAR VALLEJO

translated by H. R. Hays

ENEREIDA

My father barely,
In the bird-filled morning,
Sets his seventy-eight years, his seventy-eight
Winter branches out to sun.
The cemetery of Santiago, anointed
With happy new year is within sight.
How many times his steps have cut across it
And returned from some humble burial!

For a long time my father has not gone out.
A gang of children breaks up.

At other times he talks to my mother
About his impressions of the town, about politics;
And today, leaning on his illustrious cane,
Which sounded better during the years of his governorship,
My father is unknown, fragile;
My father is a precursor.
Absent-mindedly he picks up, he carries relics, things,

Memories, suggestions.
The peaceable morning accompanies him
On the white wings of a sister of charity.

This is an eternal day, ingenuous day, childlike,
Choral, prayerful;
Time is crowned with doves
And the future is peopled
With caravans of immortal roses.
Father, even though everything stays awake,
It is January which sings, it is your love
Which goes resounding through Eternity.
Even though you shall laugh at your little ones
And there shall be a triumphant disturbance in space.

Even though it will be the new year. There will be
Meat pies and I shall be hungry when the lyrical blind man,
With whom my fresh schoolboy syllables
And my plump innocence used to speak,
Rings for mass
In the blessed belltower.
And when the morning fills with grace,
From its breasts of time
Which are two renunciations, two surges of love—
Sing and set your plural words winging,
Shreds of your being,
On board its white,
Sister-of-charity wings, O my father!

from *Los heraldos negros*

XXXIX

Who has lit a match?
I tear my hair. I smile
Intentionally a seesaw smile.
I smile even more if they all come
To see my shabby and always pointed
Moustache. What do I care?

Nor this sun's goodness which, dying of pleasure,
Shreds everything as it distributes it
Among the shadows, the prodigal,
Nor would it wait for me on the other shore.

The tall bread-seller calls,
Ringing in the retina. And we pay with the most
Curious signs for the warm, undeniable,
Baked transcendent value.
And we drink coffee, already late,
Without enough sugar, of which there's a shortage,
And bread without butter. What shall we do?

But this is it, the hoops tightened, barred.
Health goes on one foot. Forward, march!

from *Trilce*

XIII

I think of your sex.
My heart simplified, I think of your sex,
Before the ripe crotch of day.
I touch the bud of joy, it is in season.
An ancient sentiment dies,
Degenerating in the brain.

I think of your sex, more prolific
And harmonious furrow than the belly of Darkness,
Even though Death conceives and gives birth
To God himself.

O Consciencia,
I think, indeed, of the brute at liberty
Which enjoys where it wants to, where it can.

O scandal of honey of twilights,
O mute thunder
Rednuhtetum!

from *Trilce*

LXI

Tonight, dismounting from my horse
Before the door of the house where
The cock's-crow bade me farewell—
It's closed and no one answers.

The stone seat, where mama held a light
For my eldest brother to saddle backs I had ridden bare
Through village streets and past fences, country child;
The seat on which I left my suffering childhood
Yellowing in the sun . . . and this mourning
Which marks the entrance?

God in this alien peace—
My brute sneezes as if calling, too,
Snuffs, paws the cobbles. Then doubtfully
He neighs,
Puts forward an alert ear.

We must watch papa praying and perhaps
He will think I am late.
My sisters, humming their simple
Illusions, bubbling over,
At work on the nearing fiesta,
And now there's hardly anything more to be done.
I wait, I wait, heart
Like an egg, obstructed, though all ready to be laid.

Though it was a numerous family we left
Not long ago, today no one watches, not a candle
Placed on the altar for our return.

I call again—nothing.
We are silent, we begin to weep and the animal
Neighs, keeps neighing more loudly.

They are all sleeping forever,
And it's all for the best, as at last
My tired horse ends by shaking his head
In his turn and, dreamily, with each nod says—
That it's all right, everything is quite all right.

from *Trilce*

MALAGA

Man of Estremadura,
I hear beneath your foot the smoke of the wolf,
The smoke of the spice,
The smoke of the child,
The solitary smoke of two wheats,
The smoke of Geneva, the smoke of Rome, the smoke of
    Berlin
And that of Paris, the smoke of your sad phallos,
And the smoke which at last arises from the future.
O life, O land, O Spain!
Ounces of blood,
Meters of blood, liquids of blood,
Blood on horseback, on foot, mural, without diameter,
Blood of four by four, blood of water,
And blood killed by living blood!

Estremeño, O to be even that man
By whom life kills you and death gives birth to you
Instead to be left so alone, seeing you like this, from this
    wolf,
Indeed you go on plowing our breasts!
Estremeño, you know
The secret in two voices, palpable and of the people,
The secret of grain: that nothing is worth so much
As a great root in the process of becoming another one!
Secluded estremeño, representing the soul in retirement,
Secluded while watching
A life fitted into a death!

Estremeño, and not to have earth which would have borne
The weight of your plow, nor more world
Than the color of your yoke between two epochs, not to have
The order of your posthumous flocks,
Estremeño, you allowed me
To see you suffer from this wolf,
To fight for all and to fight
To make the individual a man,
To make the gentry a man,
Even the animals men,
The reptile a man,
The vulture an honest man,
The fly a man, and the olive a man,
Even the hillock a man,
And even the sky entirely a little man.

Then, retreating from Talavera,
In groups of one, armed with hunger, in masses of one,
Armed with your breast facing forward,
Without airplanes, without war, without rancor,
Losing behind your back
And winning
Lower than lead, mortally wounded with honor,
Mad with dust, your arm on foot,
Loving by force,
Gaining all the earth in Spanish,
Still retreating and not knowing
Where to put your Spain,
Where to hide your world-kiss,
Where to plant your pocket olive!
Yet from here, later on,
From the point of view of this earth,
From the sorrow to which satanic good flows,
The great battle of Guernica can be seen.
Contest a priori, outside of the reckoning,
Contest in peace, contest of weak souls
Against weak bodies, contest in which the child strikes
Without anyone telling it to strike,

Beneath its terrible diphthong,
And beneath its most clever diaper,
And in which the mother strikes with her cry, with the back-
    edge of a tear,
And in which the sick man strikes with his disease, and with
    his pill and with his son,
And in which the old man strikes with his grey hairs, his cen-
    turies and his cane,
And in which the preacher strikes with God!
Silent defenders of Guernica!
O weak ones! O gentle offended!
May you rise up, may you grow
And fill the world with powerful weakness!

In Madrid, in Bilbao, in Santander,
The cemeteries were bombarded
And the immortal dead
With vigilant bones, with eternal shoulder, the immortal dead
From the tombs, feeling, seeing, hearing
Such baseness, such vile, dead aggressors,
Again took up their unfinished pain,
They ceased weeping, they ceased hoping,
They ceased
Suffering, they ceased living,
At last they ceased to be mortal!
And suddenly the gunpowder was nothing,
Signs and seals crossing themselves,
And from the explosion another step came walking,
And from the flight, on all fours, another step,
From the apocalyptic sky another step,
From the seven metals unity,
Simple, just, collective, eternal!

Malaga, without father or mother,
Nor pebble, no oven, nor white dog!
Malaga defenseless, where my death was born walking
And my birth died of passion!
Malaga, walking behind your feet, in exodus,

Below evil, below cowardice, below concave, unutterable his-
    tory,
With the yolk in your hand: organic earth!
And the brightness at the end of the hair: all chaos!
Malaga, flying
From father to father, domestic, from your son to your son,
Along the sea which flies from the sea,
Through the metal which flies from lead,
Along the surface of the ground which flies from the earth
And by order, ah,
Of the profundity which loved you!
Malaga, smashed, fearful clotting, by bandits, to hell-
    fragments,
To sky-fragments,
Walking over hardened wine, in a multitude,
Over the lilac foam, one by one,
Over an ecstatic hurricane, and more lilacs,
And in the compass of the four orbits that love,
And of the two ribs that kill each other!
Malaga of my diminutive blood
And my far-off color,
Life follows your sorrel-colored honors with a drum,
Your eternal children with rockets,
And your last drum with silence,
And your soul with nothing,
And your breastbone of genius with more nothing!
Malaga, do not take your name away with you!
For, if you go,
You go
Wholly, toward yourself, infinitely all in your total sound,
Consonant with your fixed stature in which I go mad,
With your fertile shoesole and the hole in it,
With your ancient knife tied to your infirm sickle
And your hammer with the handle tied to it!
Malaga, literally and malagueña,
Flying into Egypt, even though you are nailed,
Lengthening your dance in identical suffering,
Resolving the volume of the sphere in yourself,

Loosing your earthen jar, your songs flying,
With your external Spain and your inborn world!
Malaga by its own right
And in the biological garden more Malaga!
Malaga in virtue
Of the road, considering the wolf which follows you,
And by reason of the wolf cub that awaits you!
Malaga that I weep for!
Malaga that I weep and weep!

from *España, aparta de mi este caliz*

WINTER IN THE BATTLE OF TERUEL

A water of rinsed revolvers falls!
Precisely,
It is the metallic grace of water
In the late Aragon afternoon
In spite of the fabricated grass,
The burning vegetables, the industrial plants.

Precisely,
It is the serene branch of chemistry,
The explosive branch in a hair,
The automobile branch in frequencies and farewells.

So man answers, and so death,
So he looks it in the face and listens to it from the side,
So the water, the opposite of blood, is made of water,
So the fire, the reverse of ashes, smoothes its musing cold-
    congealed bodies.

Who goes there, beneath the snow? Are they killing? No.
Precisely,
Life goes on, shaking its second rope.

And war is most horrible,
It grows sluggish, heavy-eyed;
War provides tombs, it makes you fall,

It makes you give a strange ape-like leap!
You smell it comrade, perfectly,
As you tread
Absent-mindedly upon your arm among corpses;
You see it; then you touch your testicles, turning very red;
You hear it in your natural soldier's mouth.

Come along then, comrade;
Your visible shadow awaits us,
Your quartered shadow awaits us,
Midday captain, plain soldier night . . .
For this reason, as I mention this agony,
I depart from myself, crying loudly:
Down with my corpse! . . . and I sob.

from *España, aparta de mi este caliz*

SWEETNESS CROWNED

Sweetness crowned by sweetness,
Sprigs of sweetness, you were visible
On those open days when I climbed up fallen trees!
So by means of your dove little dove,
By means of your passive prayer,
Going between your shadow and the great bodily tenacity of
    your shadow.

Beneath you and me,
You and I sincerely,
Your padlock choking on keys,
I climbing and sweating
And creating the infinite between your thighs.
(The hotelkeeper is a beast,
His teeth, admirable; I control
The pallid order of my soul:
Sir, over yonder . . . step step . . . good-by, Sir . . .).

I think a great deal of this lasting commotion
And I set your dove at the height of your flight

And, limping with pleasure at times,
I rest in the shade of this destitute tree.

Rib of my thing,
Sweetness you smilingly cover with your hand;
Your black dress which shall have been worn out,
Beloved, beloved, altogether,
How united to your sick knee!

Artless I see you now, ashamed I understand you
In Letonia, Germany, Russia, Belgium, you, missing,
Your typewriter missing,
A man convulsed by the woman trembling in his fetters.

Beloved, in the shape of your irreparable behind,
Beloved that I shall love with blooming matches,
Quand on a la vie et la jeunesse
C'est déjà tellement!

When there is no space
Between your greatness and my last intention,
Beloved,
I shall return to your stocking, you have to kiss me then,
Descending by means of your repeated stocking,
Your typewriter missing, tell it this way. . . .

from *Poemas humanos*

GOOD SENSE

"Mother there is a place in the world which is called Paris. A
very large place and far off and, once again, large."

My mother fixes the collar of my coat, not because it is beginning to snow but so that it may begin to snow.

My father's woman is in love with me, coming and advancing
backward toward my birth and facing toward my death.
For I am hers twice: by farewell and by return. I close

her when I return. That is why her eyes beat me so, on a level with me, in flagranti with me, and it happens by means of finished works, by means of consummated pacts.

Is my mother dedicated to me, appointed by me? How is it she doesn't give so much to my other brothers? To Victor, for example, the eldest, who is now so old that people say he seems like his mother's younger brother! It must be because I have travelled so much! It must be because I have lived more!

My mother gives colorful credence to my stories on returning. Faced with my life of return, remembering I have travelled for two hearts through her belly, she blushes and continues to be mortally pale, when I say at the entrance of the soul: that night I was happy. But more often she grows sad, more often she would have grown sad.

"Son, how old you are!"

And she passes through the color yellow to weep because she finds me older, in the blade of the sword, in the outlet of my face. She weeps with me, she grows sad with me. What lack of my youth will she feel if I am always her son? Why do mothers suffer at growing older than their sons if the sons never reach the age of the mothers? And why, if the nearer the sons approach the end, the closer they approach the age of their parents? My mother weeps because I am old in my time and I shall never grow old in hers.

My goodbys set out from a point in her being, outside of the point in her being to which I return. I am, because of the excessive distance of my return, more man to my mother than son to my mother. In this resides the whiteness which today lights up in three flames. Then I say to her until I grow silent—

"Mother there is a place in the world which is called Paris.
    A very large place and far off and, once again, large."

My father's woman, hearing me, eats her lunch and her mortal
    eyes descend softly over my arms.

from *Poemas humanos*

THIS IS A MUTILATED MAN

There is a mutilated man who became so not in combat but
    from an embrace, not from war but from peace. He lost
    his face in love and not in hate. He lost it in the normal
    course of life and not in an accident. He lost it in the
    natural order of things and not in the disorder of men.
    Colonel Picot, president of "les gueules cassées" has a
    mouth eaten by the powder of 1914. This mutilated
    man I know has a face eaten by immortal and immemo-
    rial air.

Dead face above a living trunk. Rigid face, fastened with
    nails to the living head. This face ends by being the back
    of the skull, the skull of the skull. I once saw a tree turn
    its back to me and another time a road which turned its
    back to me. A tree with its back to you only grows in
    places where no one was ever born or died. A road with
    its back to you only goes through places where there
    have been all deaths and no births. The man, mutilated
    by peace and love, by the embrace and by order, who has
    a dead face above a living trunk was born in the shadow
    of a tree with its back turned and his existence takes
    place along a road with its back turned.

As the face is stiff and dead, all psychic life, all animal ex-
    pression in the man takes refuge, in order to express it-
    self externally, in the hairy skull, in the chest, in the ex-
    tremities. The impulses of his most profound being,
    when expressed, recede from his face and his breathing,
    his sight, his hearing, his sense of smell, his words, the

human light of his being functions and is expressed by the chest, through the shoulders, the hair, the ribs, the arms, the legs and the feet.

The face being mutilated, the face being hidden, closed, this man nevertheless is whole and lacks nothing. He has no eyes and he sees and weeps. He has no nose and he smells and breathes. He has no ears and he hears. He has no mouth and he speaks and smiles. He has no chin and he loves and subsists. Jesus knew the man with mutilated faculties who had eyes and did not see, ears and did not hear. I know the man with mutilated organs who sees without eyes and hears without ears.

from *Poemas humanos*

THE WHEEL OF THE HUNGRY

I emerge from between my own teeth, sniffing,
Crying out, pushing,
Dropping my trousers . . .
My stomach empty, my guts empty,
Poverty pulls me out from between my own teeth,
Caught on a sliver by the cuff of my shirt.

A stone to sit on,
Can't I even have that now?
Even that stone the woman who gave birth stumbles on,
The mother of the lamb, the cause, the root,
Can't I even have that one now?
At least the other one
That passed stooping through my soul.
At least the limestone, the bad one (humble ocean)
Or the one not even good to throw at a man,
Let me have that one now!

At least the one they find by chance and in an insult,
Let me have that one now!

At least the twisted and crowned one on which,
But once, resounds the tread of clear consciences,
Or at least the other, hurled in a suitable curve
In declaration of inmost truth,
Let me have that one now!

A crumb of bread, not even that for me now?
Now I just have to be what I always have to be.
But give me
A stone on which to sit,
But give me,
In Spanish,
Something, at least to eat, to drink, to live, to rest me,
And then I shall go away . . .
I discover a strange shape, my shirt is very ragged
And dirty
And still I have nothing,
This is horrible.

from *Poemas humanos*

CONSIDERING COLDLY

Considering coldly, impartially,
That man is sad, coughs, and nevertheless
Is smug in his ruddy breast
And the only thing he does is compose himself
Of days,
That he is murky, a mammal, and combs his hair . . .

Considering
That man comes softly home from work
And, re-echoing his chief, rings with a subordinate sound,
That the diagram of time
Is a constant diorama in his medals
And his half-closed eyes have studied
For a long time
His ravenous mass-formula . . .

Realizing without difficulty
That man pauses, at times, thinking,
As if wanting to weep,
And, subject to being stretched out as an object,
Becomes a good carpenter, sweats, kills,
And then sings, has lunch, buttons his buttons . . .

Considering likewise
That man is, in truth, an animal
And, just the same, turns around and hits me on the head
    with his sadness . . .

Examining finally
His hostile fragments, his privy,
His desperation at the end of his terrible day, rubbing it
    out . . .
Realizing that he knows I love him
And hate him with affection and that he, on the whole, is
    indifferent to me . . .

Considering his general documents
And looking with glasses at the certificate
Which proves he was born very small . . .

I make him a sign,
He comes
And I give him an embrace, full of tenderness.
What more can you do? Full of tenderness . . .

                              from *Poemas humanos*

THE EXCEPTION AND THE RULE

BERTOLT BRECHT
translated by Eric Bentley

Editor's Note: Die Ausnahme und die Regel, *written in 1930,
was one of the unproduced plays published in Bertolt Brecht's*
Gesammelte Werke *in 1938. It could not be properly pro-
duced until a musical score had been composed for it; Paul
Dessau's music dates from 1948. In the following year, Jean-
Marie Serreau directed the play with two groups of actors, one
French, one German, and performances were given in one
language or the other in various parts of France and Germany;
the French text appeared in Sartre's magazine* Les Temps
Modernes. *In 1950, the play was translated into Italian by
Vito Pandolfi, and was directed in that language by Eric
Bentley for the National Festival of the Drama at Bologna.
Mr. Bentley's production was toured through the cities of
Northern Italy.*

*The music of Paul Dessau had proved rather too difficult
both for Serreau's and Bentley's actors though they struggled
with it as best they could. The first time the whole score was
properly performed was in a radio production of Eric Bentley's on the national Italian radio (Radio Italiana) when the
songs were dubbed in with the voices of professional singers.*

*Eric Bentley's English version of the text was first published
in* Chrysalis, *December, 1954.*

45

CHARACTERS:

THE MERCHANT
THE GUIDE
THE COOLIE
THE INNKEEPER
THE COOLIE'S WIDOW
THE JUDGE
THE LEADER OF THE SECOND CARAVAN

TWO POLICEMEN, TWO ASSISTANTS TO THE JUDGE
MEMBERS OF THE SECOND CARAVAN

Prologue

We hereby report to you
The story of a journey, undertaken by
One who exploits and two who are exploited
Observe the conduct of these people closely:
Find it estranging even if not very strange
Hard to explain even if it is the custom
Hard to understand even if it is the rule
Observe the smallest action, seeming simple,
With mistrust
Enquire if a thing be necessary
Especially if it is common
We particularly ask you—
When a thing continually occurs—
Not on that account to find it natural
Let nothing be called natural
In an age of bloody confusion
Ordered disorder, planned caprice,
And dehumanized humanity, lest all things
Be held unalterable!

SCENE 1

THE RACE THROUGH THE DESERT

(Two separate little parties, at some distance from each other, are crossing the desert at speed.)

THE MERCHANT (*to his men, a Guide and a Coolie, the latter laden with baggage*): Hurry, you lazy dogs! In another two days we've got to be at Station Han. We've got to squeeze out a head start of one full day! (*To the audience*) I am the merchant Karl Langmann. I'm on my way to Urga to make the final arrangements for a concession. My competitors aren't very far behind, and whoever gets there first closes the deal. By my cleverness, my energetic surmounting of every obstacle, and my uncompromising attitude to the personnel, I have made the first part of the journey in half the usual time. Unfortunately, so have my competitors. (*He looks toward the rear through binoculars. To his men*) Look, they're on our heels again already! (*To the Guide only*) Why don't you drive the fellow on? I hired you to drive him hard, not to take a walk with him on my money. All right: If there's sabotage, I'll report you—at the employment agency in Urga.

THE GUIDE (*to the Coolie*): Make an effort. Faster!

THE MERCHANT: You don't have the right tone of voice, you'll never be a real guide. I should have taken a more expensive one, they always repay your investment. Go on then: hit the fellow! (*To the audience*) I'm not for beating but right now there's no other way: if I don't get there first, I'm ruined. (*To the Guide*) Confess: this carrier's your brother —*some* relation anyhow—*that's* why you don't beat him! I know you, though, I know you all from way back, and you aren't such gentle Jesuses either! Beat him or you're fired— and you can sue me for your wages! For God's sake, they'll overtake us!

THE COOLIE (*to the Guide*): Beat me, but keep some of your strength in reserve. I must keep some of *my* strength in reserve if we are supposed to reach Station Han.

(*The Guide beats the Coolie.*)

SHOUTS FROM THE REAR: Hello! Is this the way to Urga! We're friends! Wait for us!

THE MERCHANT (*neither answering nor looking back*): To hell with you! Let's go! I'll have kept my men going three days, two with curses, the third with promises, we'll see about the promises in Urga. My competitors are at my heels, but the second night I'll keep going all night, I'll get so far ahead they can't see me, we'll be at Station Han on the third day, one day ahead of all the others!

(*Sings*)   I did not sleep, therefore I soon won the lead
Kept on the move, and am now far ahead
The weak man stays behind and the strong man arrives.

SCENE 2

THE END OF A MUCH-TRAVELED ROAD

THE MERCHANT (*before Station Han*): Here is Station Han. Thank God I've reached it one day ahead of all the others. My men are exhausted. What's more, they're pretty bitter about me. They're just not interested in record-breaking. They're not fighters. They're stick-in-the-muds, nobodies, rifraff! Of course they don't dare say anything because there's still the police, thank God, to maintain order.

TWO POLICEMEN (*approaching*): Everything in order, sir? Satisfied with the roads? Satisfied with the personnel?

THE MERCHANT: Everything's in order. I made it up to here in three days instead of four. The roads are filthy but I'm a man that finishes what he sets out to do. How are the roads after Station Han? What lies before us?

THE POLICEMEN: The uninhabited Jahi desert lies before you, sir.

THE MERCHANT: Is there a police escort to be had there?

THE POLICEMEN (*passing on*): No, sir, we're the last patrol you'll see, sir.

SCENE 3

THE DISMISSAL OF THE GUIDE AT STATION HAN

THE GUIDE: Since we spoke to the police in the street in front of the station, our merchant is a changed man. The tone he

uses with us is quite different: he's friendly. This has
nothing to do with the speed of the journey because we're
not getting a day off even at this station, which is the last
before the Jahi desert. I don't know how I'm to get this
carrier all the way to Urga in such an exhausted state. All
in all, this friendly behavior on the merchant's part is very
disturbing to me. I'm afraid he's cooking something up. He
walks around lost in thought. Meditations—machinations!
And whatever he thinks out, the carrier and I will just have
to put up with it. Otherwise he'll either not pay us or simply
throw us over in mid-desert.

THE MERCHANT (*approaching*): Have some tobacco. Here's
cigarette paper. You'd go through fire for a single drag,
wouldn't you? I don't know what you people wouldn't do
to get this smoke down your throats. Thank God we've
brought enough along. Our tobacco would take us three
times as far as Urga.

THE GUIDE (*taking the tobacco, aside*): *Our* tobacco!

THE MERCHANT: Let's sit down, my friend. Why don't you sit
down? Travel brings people into a more intimate relation-
ship. Of course if you don't wish to, you can stand. You
people have your ways! In general I wouldn't sit down with
you and you wouldn't sit down with the carrier. The world
is based on such distinctions. But we can smoke together.
Can't we? (*He laughs.*) I like that about you. In its way
it's a kind of dignity. Very well, pack up the rest of the
stuff. And don't forget the water. I hear there aren't many
water holes in the desert. Another thing, my friend, I
wanted to warn you: did you notice how the carrier looked
at you when you handled him roughly? There was something in his eyes that bodes no good. But you'll have to
handle him different in the next few days, we have to in-
crease our speed still more. He's a lazy fellow, that one. The
region we're coming to is uninhabited, maybe he'll show
his true colors. Now you are a better man, you earn more
and you don't have to do any carrying: reason enough for
him to hate you. You'd be well-advised to keep away from
him. (*The Guide goes through an open door into the court-*

yard. The Merchant is left sitting alone.) Funny people!
*(The Merchant is silent and stays where he is. In the yard
the Guide supervises the Coolie's packing. Then he sits
down and smokes. When the Coolie is ready, he too sits
down, receives from his companion tobacco and cigarette
paper, and starts a conversation with him.)*

THE COOLIE: The Merchant always says it's a "service to humanity" to take oil out of the ground. When the oil is taken
out of the ground, there'll be railroads here, and prosperity
will spread. The Merchant says there'll be railroads. How
shall I earn my living?

THE GUIDE: Don't worry. There won't be railroads as quickly
as all that. They discover oil, and then they suppress the
discovery, or so I've heard. The man who stops up the oil
hole gets hush-money. That's why the Merchant is in such
a hurry. It's not the oil he's after, it's the hush-money.

THE COOLIE: I don't understand.

THE GUIDE: No one understands.

THE COOLIE: The path across the desert is sure to get even
worse. I hope my feet will hold out.

THE GUIDE: Certainly.

THE COOLIE: Are there bandits?

THE GUIDE: We'll have to keep a lookout—especially today,
the first day of the trip. The station attracts every sort of
rabble.

THE COOLIE: How about afterwards?

THE GUIDE: Once we have the Myr river behind us, it's a matter of sticking to the water holes.

THE COOLIE: You know the way?

THE GUIDE: Yes. *(The Merchant has heard voices. He comes
up behind the door to listen.)*

THE COOLIE: Is the Myr river hard to cross?

THE GUIDE: Not in general—at this time of year. But when
it's in flood, the current is very strong, and you take your
life in your hands.

THE MERCHANT: So he's talking to the carrier. He can sit down
with *him*. He's smoking with him!

THE COOLIE: What do you do then?

THE GUIDE: You often have to wait a week or so to get safely across.

THE MERCHANT: Well, well, well! He even advises him to take his time and hold on to his precious life! A dangerous fellow, that one. He'd only back his coolie up. In any case, not the man to put the job through. No telling what he might do either. In short: as of today, they're two against one. At any rate, it's clear he's afraid to boss his own underlings now we're entering uninhabited territory. I must definitely get rid of the fellow. (*He joins the other two.*) I gave you the assignment of checking if the things are properly packed. Let's see how you carry out my assignments. (*He takes hold of a strap and gives it a terrific pull. It breaks.*) Call that packing? Breaking a strap means a day's delay. But that's just what you want: delay!

THE GUIDE: I do not want delay. And the straps don't break if you don't pull them like that.

THE MERCHANT: What? Is the strap broken or not? Just you dare tell me to my face it's not broken! You are unreliable. I made a mistake treating you decently, you people don't appreciate it. I've no use for a guide who can't command the respect of the personnel. It seems to me you should be a carrier, not a guide. There are grounds for believing you stir up the personnel.

THE GUIDE: What grounds?

THE MERCHANT: You'd like to know, wouldn't you? Very well: you're dismissed!

THE GUIDE: But you can't dismiss me when we're halfway there.

THE MERCHANT: Think yourself lucky if I don't report you at the agency in Urga. Here are your wages, up to this point of course. (*Shouts to the Innkeeper who enters*) You are my witness: I paid him his wages. (*To the Guide*) And let me tell you something: you'd better not show your face in Urga any more! (*Looks him over from top to toe*) You'll never get anywhere. (*He goes into the other room with the Innkeeper.*) I set out at once. If anything happens to me, you are my witness that today I set out alone with that man.

(*He points to the Coolie. The Innkeeper indicates with gestures that he understands nothing. The Merchant is taken aback. To the audience*) He doesn't understand. In that case there'll be no one to say where I went. And the worst of it is these fellows *know* there'll be no one. (*He sits down and writes a letter.*)

THE GUIDE (*to the Coolie*): I made a mistake sitting down with you. Take care: he's bad, that man. (*He gives him his water flask.*) Keep this flask in reserve. Hide it. If you get lost—and you will—he's sure to take yours. I'll explain the road to you.

THE COOLIE: I don't think you should. He mustn't hear you talking to me. If he throws me out, I'm done for. He doesn't even have to pay me. I'm not in a union like you, I must put up with everything.

THE MERCHANT (*to the Innkeeper*): Give this letter to the people who'll be arriving here tomorrow on their way to Urga. I'm going on ahead with my carrier and no one else.

THE INNKEEPER (*nodding and taking the letter*): But he isn't a guide.

THE MERCHANT (*to himself*): So he does understand, he just didn't want to admit it. He knows how things are, he simply has no intention of being a witness in such cases. (*To the Innkeeper, peremptorily*) Explain the way to Urga to my carrier. (*The Innkeeper goes outside and explains the way to Urga to the Coolie. The Coolie nods eagerly a number of times.*) I see there'll be a struggle. (*He takes out his revolver and cleans it, singing.*)

The sick man dies and the strong man fights
Wherefore should the earth yield the oil, say wherefore?
And why should the Coolie my baggage carry?
For oil we must struggle both
With the earth and with the Coolie
What the struggle means is this:
The sick man dies and the strong man fights.

(*He goes into the courtyard, ready to leave.*) Do you know the way now?

THE COOLIE: Yes, Master.

THE MERCHANT: Then let's go. (*The Merchant and the Coolie go. The Innkeeper and the Guide watch.*)

THE GUIDE: I don't know if the Coolie understood. He understood too quickly.

SCENE 4

A CONVERSATION IN DANGEROUS TERRITORY

THE COOLIE (*singing*):

> I'm going to the town of Urga
> Nothing will stop me going to Urga
> No bandit can keep me from the town of Urga
> The desert will not hold me back from Urga
> There is food in the town of Urga and pay.

THE MERCHANT: This coolie isn't worried, oh no! There are bandits in this part of the country—the station attracts all sorts of rabble. And he sings! (*To the Coolie*) I never did like that guide. One day insubordinate, the next licking my boots. Not an honest man.

THE COOLIE: Yes, Master. (*Singing again*)

> The road is hard to Urga
> I hope my feet hold all the way to Urga
> The pain is enormous on the road to Urga
> But in Urga there is rest and pay.

THE MERCHANT: Now just why do you sing? What are you so cheery about, my friend? You really aren't afraid of robbers? What they could take doesn't belong to you, what *you* have to lose belongs to me. That it?

THE COOLIE (*sings*):

> My wife also awaits me in Urga
> My little son also awaits me in Urga
> Also . . .

THE MERCHANT (*interrupting him*): I don't like that singing! We have no reason to sing. They can hear you all the way to Urga. That's how to attract the attention of the rabble. Tomorrow you can sing as much as you want.

THE COOLIE: Yes, Master.

THE MERCHANT (*now walking in front of him*): He wouldn't defend himself for one second if anyone tried to take his things away. What would he do? If my property is in danger, it's his duty to defend it like his own. But he wouldn't. Never. A bad lot. He never says anything. That kind are the worst. I wish I could see into his mind. What's he planning to do? He has nothing to laugh about and he laughs. What at? Why, for instance, does he have me walk ahead of him? *He's* the one that knows the way. And where is he taking me? (*He looks around and sees the Coolie wiping out their footprints in the sand.*) What's that you're doing?

THE COOLIE: Wiping out our footprints, Master.

THE MERCHANT: And why, may I ask?

THE COOLIE: On account of the bandits.

THE MERCHANT: I see, on account of the bandits. But I want it to be clear where you've taken me. Where *are* you taking me anyway? You go first! (*The Coolie now walks in front of the Merchant. Silence. Then the Merchant says to himself:*) In this sand our footprints really are very easy to see. Actually, of course, it would be a good thing to wipe out our footprints.

SCENE 5

AT THE RUSHING RIVER

THE COOLIE: We've been on the right road, Master. What we see there is the Myr river. In general, at this time of year, the river isn't hard to cross but, when it's in flood, the current is very strong, and you take your life in your hands.

THE MERCHANT: We must get across.

THE COOLIE: You often have to wait a week or so to safely get across. At present you take your life in your hands.

THE MERCHANT: We'll see about that. We can't wait a single day.

THE COOLIE: Then we'll have to look for a ford—or a boat.

THE MERCHANT: It takes too much time.

THE COOLIE: But I can't swim properly.

THE MERCHANT: The water isn't very high.

THE COOLIE (*lowers a stick in the water*): It is very high.

THE MERCHANT: Once you're in the water, you'll swim all right, you'll have to. You can't see the matter from all sides like me, see what I mean? Why must we get to Urga? Are you too much of a fool to understand it's doing mankind a service to extract oil from the earth? When the oil is extracted, there'll be railways here and prosperity will spread. There'll be bread and clothes and heaven knows what. And who will bring this about? *We* shall. It all depends on *our* journey. Just imagine: the eyes of the whole country are on you—a little man like you! And you hesitate to do your duty?

THE COOLIE (*has been nodding respectfully during this speech*): I can't swim properly.

THE MERCHANT: I risk my life too. (*The Coolie nods overawed.*) I don't understand you. Prompted by low considerations of pecuniary gain, you have no interest in reaching Urga as soon as possible. Your interest is to get there as late as possible—because you're paid by the day. In fact it isn't the journey that interests you, it's the pay!

THE COOLIE (*stands hesitating at the river bank*): What am I to do?

(*Sings*) Here is the river
To swim across is dangerous
On the bank there stand two men
And one swims across it, the other
Hesitates
Is one brave? Is the other a coward?
Across the river
One of the two has business
From the danger one emerges
Smiling
On the bank he has conquered
Setting foot on his property
And eating new food

Alas, the other from the danger emerges
Panting
Into nothing
Weaker now, new dangers lie in his path
Are both men courageous?
Are they both wise?
They conquered the river together but
Are not both conquerors
"We" and "you and me"
They are not the same
We defeat the foe
And you defeat me.

At least let me rest for half a day. I'm tired from all the carrying. Maybe after a rest, I *can* get across.

THE MERCHANT: I know a better solution: You'll get my revolver in your back. Shall we bet you get across? (*He pushes him on. To himself*) My money makes me fear bandits and overlook the dangerous state of the river.

(*Sings*) In this way man masters the desert and the rushing river
Man masters man himself
The oil, the needed oil, is his reward.

SCENE 6

THE BIVOUAC

(*It is evening, and the Coolie, whose arm is broken, is trying to pitch the tent. The Merchant is sitting nearby.*)

THE MERCHANT: But I told you, you don't need to put the tent up today—after breaking your arm crossing the river. (*The Coolie goes on putting it up and does not speak.*) If I hadn't pulled you out of the water you'd have drowned. (*The Coolie goes on.*) Though of course, I am not responsible for your accident—the tree might just as easily have hit *me*—all the same the mishap befell you during a journey in my company. I have very little cash on me. My bank is in Urga. When we arrive, I'll give you some money.

THE COOLIE: Yes, Master.

THE MERCHANT: He doesn't waste words. And with every look he gives me to understand that I'm the cause of his misfortune. A malicious lot, these coolies! (*To the Coolie*) You can lie down. (*He walks away and sits down at a distance.*) It's clear that his mishap makes more difference to me than to him. The rabble don't much bother whether they're maimed or whole. So long as they can eat, they're satisfied. Their natural limitations keep them from bothering their heads about themselves any further. They're failures. Now, if you make something and it turns out a failure you throw it away. They, *being* failures, throw themselves away. It's the hundred percenter who fights!

 (*Sings*) The sick man dies and the strong man fights
     And that's how it should be
     All aid to the strong man and none to the weak
     That's how it should be
     What falls—let it fall—then give it a kick
     For that's how it should be
     He sits down to dinner who the battle has won
     That's how it should be
     And the conqueror's cook makes no count of the
      slain
     And that's how it should be
     And the god of things as they are made master
      and man
     And that's how it should be
     Who has good luck is good and who has bad luck
      is bad
     And that's how it should be.

(*The Coolie has approached. The Merchant notices him and is startled.*) He's been listening! Stop! Stay where you are! What do you want?

THE COOLIE: The tent is ready, Master.

THE MERCHANT: Don't sneak about in the night. I don't like it. When a man comes to me, I like to hear his footsteps. And I want to look him in the eye when I talk to him. You lie down, and don't trouble yourself so much about me. (*The*

Coolie goes back.) Stop! You go into the tent! I'll sit here because I'm used to the fresh air. (*The Coolie goes into the tent.*) I wish I knew how much he heard of my song. (*Pause*) What's he doing now? He's still busy. (*The Coolie is seen carefully preparing his "bed."*)

THE COOLIE: I hope he doesn't notice anything. With one arm, I can't cut grass properly.

THE MERCHANT: Stupid not to be on guard. To trust people is stupid. Through me, this man has been hurt—possibly damaged for the rest of his life. From his point of view, it's only right if he pays me back. And a strong man asleep is no stronger than a weak man asleep. Men shouldn't have to sleep! Certainly it would be better to sit in the tent. In the open you're a prey to every sort of sickness. But what sickness could be as dangerous as this man is! He walks at my side for little money—and I have much money—and the road is equally difficult for us both. When he was tired, he was beaten. When the Guide sat down with him, the Guide was dismissed. When he wiped out footprints in the sand— perhaps really because of bandits—he was treated with suspicion. When he showed fear at the river, he was given my revolver to look at. How can I sleep in the same tent with such a man? He can't make me believe he'll just put up with it all! I'd like to know what he's thinking up in there now! (*The Coolie is seen peacefully lying down to sleep.*) I'd be a fool to go into the tent!

SCENE 7

THE SHARED WATER

A

THE MERCHANT: What are you stopping for?

THE COOLIE: Master, the road ends here.

THE MERCHANT: Well?

THE COOLIE: Master, if you beat me, don't beat me on my sore arm. I don't know the way from here on.

THE MERCHANT: But the man at Station Han explained it to you.

THE COOLIE: Yes, Master.

THE MERCHANT: When I asked you if you understood him, you said yes.

THE COOLIE: Yes, Master.

THE MERCHANT: And you did not understand him?

THE COOLIE: No, Master.

THE MERCHANT: Then why did you say yes?

THE COOLIE: I was afraid you'd throw me out. I only know it's supposed to be along the water holes.

THE MERCHANT: Then go along the water holes.

THE COOLIE: But I don't know where they are.

THE MERCHANT: Get moving! And don't try to make a fool of me. I know you've travelled this road before. (*They walk on.*)

THE COOLIE: But wouldn't it be better to wait for that other caravan?

THE MERCHANT: No. (*They walk on.*)

B

THE MERCHANT: Where do you think you're going now? That's north, the east is *there!* (*The Coolie proceeds in that direction.*) Stop! What's the matter with you? (*The Coolie stops but does not look at the Merchant.*) Why don't you look me in the eyes?

THE COOLIE: I thought the east was there.

THE MERCHANT: Just you wait, my lad! I'll show you how to guide me. (*He beats him.*) Do you know now where the east is?

THE COOLIE (*screaming*): Not on that arm.

THE MERCHANT: Where's the east?

THE COOLIE: There.

THE MERCHANT: And where are the water holes?

THE COOLIE: There.

THE MERCHANT (*furious*): There? But you were going *there!*

THE COOLIE: No, Master.

THE MERCHANT: Aha! So you were not going there? Were you going *there*? (*He beats him.*)

THE COOLIE: Yes, Master.

THE MERCHANT: Where are the water holes? (*The Coolie is silent. The Merchant seems calm.*) You said just now you know where the water holes are? *Do* you know? (*The Coolie is silent.*)

THE MERCHANT (*beating him*): Do you know?

THE COOLIE: Yes.

THE MERCHANT (*beating him*): Do you know?

THE COOLIE: No.

THE MERCHANT: Give me your flask. (*The Coolie gives it to him.*) I could now take the view that all the water belongs to me because you guided me wrong. But I won't! I'll share the water with you. Take a swallow, and then push on. (*To himself*) I forgot myself: I oughtn't to have beaten him in this situation.

c

THE MERCHANT: We were here before. Look, our footprints!

THE COOLIE: When we were here we must have been near the right road.

THE MERCHANT: Pitch the tent. Our flask is empty, there's nothing left. (*The Merchant sits down while the Coolie pitches the tent. The Merchant drinks secretly out of his bottle. To himself*) He mustn't notice that I still have something to drink. Otherwise, if he's got a spark of understanding in his thick skull, he'll do me in. If he comes close, I shoot. (*He takes out his revolver and places it on his knees.*) If we could only reach the last water hole! I'm nearly strangled with thirst. How long can a man stand thirst?

THE COOLIE: I must hand over to him the flask that the Guide at the station gave me. Otherwise, if they find us, me still alive and him half dead, they'll put me on trial. (*He takes the bottle and walks towards the Merchant. The Merchant suddenly discovers the Coolie in front of him and doesn't know if the Coolie has seen him drink or not. The Coolie has not seen him drink. In silence, he holds out the flask to him. But the Merchant, thinking that it is one of the big stones of the countryside and that the Coolie, enraged, wants to kill him, cries out loudly.)*

THE MERCHANT: Put that stone down! (*And with a single shot from his revolver he brings down the Coolie who, not understanding, continues to hold out the flask.*) I was right. There, you bastard! You have what you asked for.

SCENE 8

THE SONG OF THE TRIBUNALS

In the wake of thief and bandit
Travel the tribunals
And when an innocent man is murdered
Judges gather round about his corpse and condemn him
At the grave of the murdered man
All his rights are murdered
The words of the tribunal
Fall like the shadow of a knife
And the knife, alas, is quite strong enough
What need after this of a verdict?
Overhead fly the vultures but whither?
The bare and barren desert repelled them:
The tribunals will give them their food
Thither flees the assassin
The persecutor finds there a sanctuary
And there the thief hides away what he has stolen
And wraps it in a piece of paper
On the which a law is written.

SCENE 9

THE TRIBUNAL

(*The Guide, the Coolie's Widow, and the Innkeeper are already sitting in the courtroom.*)

THE GUIDE (*to the Widow*): Are you the Coolie's widow? I am the guide who engaged your husband. I've heard that you are demanding the punishment of the Merchant and damages. I came to this law court right away because I have the proof that your husband was innocent. It's in my pocket.

THE INNKEEPER (*To the Guide*): I hear you have a proof in your pocket. Let me give you a piece of advice: leave it in your pocket.

THE GUIDE: Is the Coolie's widow to go away empty-handed?

THE INNKEEPER: Do you want to be blacklisted?

THE GUIDE: I'll think it over. (*The Judge and two colleagues take their seats. So does the accused Merchant. Also the Innkeeper and the members of the second caravan.*)

THE JUDGE: I declare the proceedings open. The widow of the deceased has the floor.

THE WIDOW: My husband carried this gentleman's baggage through the Jahi desert. Shortly before the end of the journey, his master shot him down. Even though my husband can't be brought back to life thereby, I demand that his murderer be punished!

THE JUDGE: You are also demanding damages.

THE WIDOW: Yes. My little son and myself have lost our breadwinner.

THE JUDGE (*to the Widow*): The material part of the claim is nothing to be ashamed of. I'm not reproaching you with it. (*To the members of the second caravan*) Behind the expedition of the merchant Karl Langmann came another expedition—joined by the guide who had been dismissed from the first expedition. They sighted the stranded expedition barely a mile from the route. What did you see as you approached?

THE LEADER OF THE SECOND CARAVAN: The Merchant had very little water left in his flask. And his carrier lay dead on the sand.

THE JUDGE (*To the Merchant*): Did you shoot the man?

THE MERCHANT: Yes. He attacked me unawares.

THE JUDGE: How did he attack you?

THE MERCHANT: He intended to strike me down from behind with a stone.

THE JUDGE: Can you explain the motive of his attack?

THE MERCHANT: No.

THE JUDGE: Did you drive your men very hard?

THE MERCHANT: No.

THE JUDGE: Is the guide present who made the first part of the journey and was dismissed?

THE GUIDE: Present!

THE JUDGE: What have you to say?

THE GUIDE: As far as I know, the important thing for the merchant was to be in Urga as soon as possible on account of a concession.

THE JUDGE (*to the Merchant*): Had you the impression that the expedition behind you maintained an unusually high speed?

THE MERCHANT: Not unusually. We had a full day's start and kept it up.

THE JUDGE (*To the Merchant*): Then you *must* have driven them hard.

THE MERCHANT: I *didn't* drive them hard. That was the Guide's job.

THE JUDGE (*To the Guide*): Did the accused make a point of telling you to drive the carrier especially hard?

THE GUIDE: I didn't drive them harder than the usual. Maybe less hard.

THE JUDGE: Why were you dismissed?

THE GUIDE: Because in the Merchant's opinion my attitude to the Coolie was too friendly.

THE JUDGE: And you shouldn't be so friendly? Did you have the impression that this Coolie who was not to be given friendly treatment was a malcontent?

THE GUIDE: No. He put up with everything because, as he told me himself, he was afraid of losing his job: he didn't belong to a union.

THE JUDGE: Did he have a lot to put up with? Answer! And don't be thinking over your answers all the time! The truth will out!

THE GUIDE: I was only with him as far as Station Han.

THE INNKEEPER (*to himself*): That's the way to talk to them.

THE JUDGE (*To the Merchant*): Did anything occur afterwards that could explain the Coolie's attack?

THE MERCHANT: No. On my side, nothing.

THE JUDGE: My good fellow, don't paint yourself whiter than you really are, you won't get off that way. If you handled your Coolie with kid gloves on, how do you explain his hatred for you? Obviously, you can only make us believe that you acted in self-defense if you also make us believe in the Coolie's hatred. Use your head!

THE MERCHANT: I must confess something. I did beat him one time.

THE JUDGE: Aha! And you believe that such hatred on the Coolie's part was occasioned by this one event?

THE MERCHANT: No. I let him have my revolver in his back when he didn't want to cross the river. It's also true that he broke his arm during the crossing. That too was my fault.

THE JUDGE (*smiling*): In the Coolie's opinion.

THE MERCHANT (*also smiling*): Of course. Actually, I helped him out of the water.

THE JUDGE: Very well. *After* the dismissal of the guide you gave the Coolie occasion to hate you. And beforehand? (*To the Guide, insisting*) Admit, after all, that the man hated the Merchant! A moment's thought makes it quite obvious. It stands to reason that a man who is badly paid, who is forcibly driven into danger, whose very health is impaired for another's gain, who risks his life for almost nothing—it stands to reason that he should hate him!

THE GUIDE: He didn't hate him.

THE JUDGE: We would like now to cross-question the Innkeeper of Station Han. Perhaps his report will give us an idea of the Merchant's relations with his personnel. (*To the Innkeeper*) How did the Merchant treat his men?

THE INNKEEPER: Well.

THE JUDGE: Shall I clear the court? Do you think you'll be damaged in the conduct of your business if you tell the truth?

THE INNKEEPER: No. In the present case, it isn't necessary.

THE JUDGE: As you wish.

THE INNKEEPER: He even gave the Guide tobacco and paid his wages in full without making trouble. And the Coolie was well-treated too.

THE JUDGE: Your station is the last police station on this route?

THE INNKEEPER: Yes, that's where the uninhabited Jahi desert begins.

THE JUDGE: I see. This friendliness of the Merchant's was more or less imposed by circumstances, was not destined to last—a strategic friendliness, so to speak. It reminds me of our officers during the war. They made it their business to be kinder and kinder to their men the nearer they got to the front. Friendship of this sort doesn't count, of course.

THE MERCHANT: For example: he'd been forever singing along the way. From the moment when I threatened him with the revolver—to get him across the river—I never heard him sing again.

THE JUDGE: He must have been completely embittered. It's quite understandable. Again I must refer to the war. In wartime one could understand the men saying to us officers: *You* fight for yourselves, but *we* fight for you! And likewise the Coolie could say to the Merchant: You do business for yourself, but I do business for you!

THE MERCHANT: I must make another confession. When we got lost I shared one flask of water with him but I intended to drink the second myself.

THE JUDGE: Did he see you drinking maybe?

THE MERCHANT: I assumed he did—when he came towards me with the stone in his hand. I knew he hated me. When we came to uninhabited territory I was on guard day and night. I had to assume that he would fall on me at the first opportunity. If I hadn't killed him, he would have killed me.

THE WIDOW: I would like to say something. He can't have attacked him. He never attacked anybody.

THE GUIDE: Keep calm. I have the proof of his innocence in my pocket.

THE JUDGE: Has the stone with which the Coolie threatened you been found yet?

THE LEADER: That man (*pointing to the Guide*) took it out

of the dead man's hand. (*The Guide shows the flask.*)

THE JUDGE: Is that the stone? Do you recognize it?

THE MERCHANT: Yes, that's the stone.

THE GUIDE: Then look what is in the stone. (*Pours water*)

FIRST COLLEAGUE: It's a water-flask and not a stone. He was handing you water.

SECOND COLLEAGUE: It certainly looks now as if he hadn't wanted to kill him at all.

THE GUIDE: (*embracing the Widow*): You see now: I was able to prove it. He was innocent. It is exceptional but I was able to prove it. I gave him the flask when he set out from the last station. The Innkeeper is my witness: this is my flask.

THE INNKEEPER (*to himself*): Fool! Now *he's* done for!

THE JUDGE: That cannot be the truth. (*To the Merchant*) Are we to believe he gave you something to drink?

THE MERCHANT: It must have been a stone.

THE JUDGE: No, it was not a stone. You can see for yourself it was a flask.

THE MERCHANT: But I couldn't *assume* that it was a flask. The man had no reason to give me something to drink. I wasn't his friend.

THE GUIDE: But he did give him something to drink!

THE JUDGE: But why did he give him something to drink? Why?

THE GUIDE: I suppose because he thought the Merchant was thirsty. (*The Judges exchange smiles.*) Probably because he was human. (*The Judges smile.*) Perhaps because he was stupid—I think he had nothing against the Merchant.

THE MERCHANT: Then he must have been *very* stupid. The man had been hurt through me, possibly for the rest of his life. His arm. It was only right if he wanted to pay me back.

THE GUIDE: It was only right.

THE MERCHANT: He walked at my side for little money—and I have much money. But the road was equally difficult for us both.

THE GUIDE (*to himself*): So he knows!

THE MERCHANT: When he was tired he was beaten.

THE GUIDE: And that is wrong?

THE MERCHANT: To assume that the Coolie would not strike me down at the first opportunity would have been to assume he had lost his reason.

THE JUDGE: You mean you assumed with justification that the Coolie must have had something against you. You may, then, have killed a man who possibly was harmless—because you couldn't *know* him to be harmless. This happens also with the police at times. They shoot into a crowd of demonstrators—quite peaceful folk—because they can't see why these folk don't simply drag them off their horses and lynch them. Actually, the police in such cases fire out of pure fear. And that they are afraid is proof of their good sense. You mean you couldn't know the Coolie was an exception!

THE MERCHANT: One must go by the rule, not by the exception.

THE JUDGE: Exactly. What reason could this Coolie have had to give his tormentor something to drink?

THE GUIDE: No sensible reason.

THE JUDGE (*singing*):
This is the rule: an eye for an eye!
The fool waits for the exception
The man of sense does not expect
That his enemy should give him to drink.

THE GUIDE (*sings*):
For in the system which they created
Humanity is an exception
And who performs a human act
Must pay the penalty
O fear for every man who seems to be friendly!
Hold him back if he tries to help someone!
Close at hand a man is thirsty, close quickly your eyes!
And close your ears, close at hand someone is groaning!
And hold back your feet: someone calls for assistance!
Woe to him, woe to him, who forgets this!
He gives a man to drink
And a wolf drinks.

THE JUDGE: The Court takes counsel. (*The Judge and two colleagues withdraw.*)

THE LEADER OF THE SECOND CARAVAN: Aren't you afraid of never getting another job?

THE GUIDE: I had to tell the truth.

THE LEADER OF THE SECOND CARAVAN (*smiling*): Oh, you had to, had you? (*The Judge and his colleagues return.*)

THE JUDGE (*to the Merchant*): The court has another question to put to you. Is it possible that you had something to gain by shooting the Coolie?

THE MERCHANT: On the contrary. I needed him for the business on hand in Urga. He carried the maps and surveying instruments which I needed. I wasn't in a position to carry my things alone.

THE JUDGE: Then you didn't close the deal in Urga?

THE MERCHANT: Of course not. I was late. I am ruined.

THE JUDGE: Then I pronounce the verdict. The court regards it as proven that the Coolie approached his master not with a stone but with a water-flask. But even when this is granted, it is more credible that the Coolie wished to kill his master with the flask than that he wished to give him something to drink. The carrier belonged to a class which has indeed motive to feel itself handicapped. For men like the Coolie it was nothing short of good sense to protect himself against an unequal distribution of the water. Yes, to these people with their narrow and one-sided outlook, an outlook, moreover, that embraces only the external realities, it must even seem just to avenge oneself on one's tormentor. On the day of reckoning they have everything to gain. The Merchant did not belong to the same class as his carrier. He had therefore, to expect the worst from him. The Merchant could not believe in an act of comradeship on the part of a carrier whom, as he has confessed, he had brutalized. Good sense told him he was threatened in the highest degree. The uninhabited character of the territory must perforce have filled him with apprehension. The absence of police and laws made it possible for his employee to seize his share of the water—nay, encouraged him to do so. The accused acted, therefore, in justifiable self-defense—it being a matter of indifference whether he was threatened or must *feel* himself threatened. In the circumstances he had to feel himself threatened. The accused is therefore acquitted. The plea of the Carrier's Widow is dismissed.

EPILOGUE

So ends
The story of a journey
You have heard and you have seen
You have seen what is common, what continually occurs
But we ask you:
Even if it's not very strange, find it estranging
Even if it is usual, find it hard to explain
What here is common should astonish you
What here's the rule, recognize as an abuse
And where you have recognized an abuse
Provide redress!

AN AFTERNOON WITH THE APPLIANCES

HERBERT GOLD

*"BUY ME IN PIECES. I AM YOUNG AND TENDER.
KILLED FRESH DAILY."*—SIGN OVER A POULTRY SHOP ON
WOODLAND AVENUE IN CLEVELAND, OHIO

Sidney Jones, wondering if amounting to appliances was
amounting to enough, shook open the door of his place over
the warped spot and entered to take the regular six-months inventory. Past his corner, and a furnace-repair shop, a pop-and-
candy stand, a homeopathic drugstore, the Nearer-to-Thee
Spiritualist Church, Inc., and a lawyer-notary office, the block
was deserted on that first June afternoon in Cleveland. He
left the door ajar, a shaft of dust-infected sun fuming a slant
across the painted floor, while he counted aloud: "The pop-up
toaster. The waffle irons, single and double. The Mixmasters
with the attachments. The picture frame lights up when you
press the button. The nighty-night lamp, kids-love-em, plays
rockabye. That item's dead," he murmured to himself, putting
an *x* near it in the ledger as his voice droned on: "The electric chimes for modern homemakers. The wake-ur-self clock
with radio attachment. The—"

Outside, Cousin Street dozed in the Sunday stillness. Even

the busses did not run today. Irma and Archie would have told him to shut the door, despite the June sun falling dry and warm on his back, but he was new enough to business to insist, "A business man keeps his doors open so the people can see him, stop and chat, make friends. Sunday friends make Monday sales. You can never tell, but take a chance even on Sunday, otherwise you *never* amount to anything."

"All right, you're amounting," Irma said.

Still, this neighborhood was something to worry about. Standing with his green ledger in a hand from which the pink calluses had almost entirely faded, he felt an uneasiness mixed with his pride at now having something to protect. It was the same uneasiness that he felt mixed with Irma's pride at their home in a neighborhood with doctors, lawyers, teachers, and only one barking revival preacher and a few captains of the numbers—almost all professional men with education. Even Buster Burwin, not the hair-straightener or a skin-bleaching type, looked like a serious man with the steel frames to his glasses, squint-eyed from genuine close-work reading of the Dow Jones averages which gave the day's numbers. Sidney himself had moved off a Western Union bicycle to a war job at Batson Products ("No Racial Prejudice at Batco For the Duration"), and then had parlayed his overtime and his passionate sobriety into *Sidney's Appliances* on Cousin Street near the chanting Spiritualists who pointed out that "He Is Your Only Savior, Your Atomic Flame-Thrower"—a disgrace to the neighborhood, although nothing was done about them. Archie Walker at the pop-and-candy stand advised him not to tangle with religion. All authority was religion for old Archie. Now, however, Sidney decided on the wisdom of Archie's motto: "Don't tangle."

When the man called Cash stepped in, Sidney had finished with the small items and had become absorbed in the big ones, the teevees, washing machines, driers, and such. "Whyncha leave the *teevee* in the window nights, Sid?" Cash asked to awaken him from his counting and his sums.

Sidney could not recall this tall, stooped idler with a tooth-pick between his yellow lips and a thin, diseased voice despite the swollen Adam's apple. A little man with a pudgy, pouting face and a rolled-up newspaper under his arm had followed Cash inside; his double-breasted jacket flopped open and frowned about his hips. Behind the little man stood a thin youth wearing part of a doorman's uniform, pale-blue braid along the outer seams of his dark-blue pants; he had a pasty, pretty, movie-usher face with thick, oily lashes and dark, girlish eyes.

Sidney looked first to the deserted street—now there was an automobile parked in the sun just opposite his store—and then to the telephone on his desk, a black tube in a glossy cradle through which he might find a friend. He used it to call the credit bureau, to call customers, and to call Irma. He wondered if it would be worth trying now. His children had a father who worried about business, just like the fathers out in Lakewood or Cleveland Heights. He had grown a moustache and, above the steel-rimmed glasses, combed his hair long with hardly any pomade. His appearance was his career, his career his life, and this series of approximations was approaching the perfection of his appliances. Now, by moving fast, maybe he could almost reach the telephone in time, maybe and almost. He paused to think of old Archie with his motto: "Don't tangle. Listen, son, don't tangle and wait it through."

Almost and maybe, Sidney Jones was thinking.

"Say, Sid," Cash whined through the sodden toothpick, "whyncha leave the *tee*vee in the window, whyncha nights?"

They had been there ten minutes already. Sidney had already put down the ledger and was waiting for them to finish with their fun. Not wanting to take his eyes from the telephone, he nonetheless looked at Cash again to remark, "It's a temptation so close like that. They broke in twice already. What did you say your name was?" He wondered whether having a nice inventory and a house was worth having this, too.

"*They* broke in," Cash said. "That's a way of putting it."

"So he keeps it on its behind on the floor," said the short, fat man with the newspaper, "out of temptation, the teevee."

The tall, stooped, sick-voiced man who said his name was Cash and asked for credit was a white man. His friend with the tightly-rolled newspaper was also a white man. Their sulky, girlish friend at the door was a white man. Their friend outside in the automobile, nervously peeking from under his cap through the door on which had been lettered, *Sidney Jones, Credit Appliances,* "A Friendly Place to Buy," was a white man.

Cash gazed at Sidney from his soft, sad eyes, which were surrounded by rings of spongy, purplish flesh out of place on his spare frame. He moved the toothpick with his tongue, and then asked slowly, "What do you mean, 'friendly?' A white man wouldn't be so friendly to his customers? An ofay? That ain't a nice thing to put in writing, Sid."

"Tactless," the liquid-eyed doorman agreed.

"Unfair competition," said Cash.

"I'm sorry, sir," Sidney explained once more. "I can give you credit on the Bendix washing machine, the automatic drier, the large-screen television, big items like that, even the Sunbeam Mixmaster, but they don't allow me to give credit on the irons, the portable radios——the smaller items. Anyway, I can't sell you anything on Sunday. I can't call the credit bureau."

"He says he won't sell us *any*thing on Sunday," the short, bald man with the newspaper said.

The doorman remarked thoughtfully, "He says he wants to call the credit bureau."

"Never mind," said Cash, while the man in the automobile came out, stood at the door and waited. He wore a cap covered with buttons—BLOOMER GIRLS, HIYA KID, HOLD-ME-TIGHT. When he took it off, Sidney was surprised to find that he was completely bald. He made a combing motion over his scalp with two fingers and replaced the cap. "We don't need anything today," said Cash. "We'll take in a show instead. Shut the door. Shut the grates. Shut the curtains." The other three were busy, the doorman's braided pants zipping together as he moved to pull the drapes hung on clothesline, and when they had finished the driver came inside.

Sidney shifted himself in front of his green inventory ledger in order to hide it, and then realized that this was the wrong thing to protect. It didn't amount to anything. He moved away. "What do you fellows want?" he asked. He thought that it was better not to try for the telephone, and at the same moment he wondered at the foolish words singing in his head, cadenced as if lifted on a jukebox bass: "Red Sands, Red Sands of Carolina. . . ." His habit was to keep his mind on business.

Cash smiled for the first time in the dusk of the darkened store, showing the sodden wood of the toothpick spread against his lip. It was Sunday afternoon outside, the still Sunday of June when Sidney had thought to make his midyear inventory, but inside now it was evening, with slats of gray light falling through the worn places in the drapes at the window. *"Fellows,* he said," Cash remarked to Sidney. Looking straight at him, he said, "He shouldn't ought to of called us the fellows. Whyncha turn us on some light, Sid, whyncha? No, you do it."

The short man, still carrying his newspaper, flicked the switch. He seemed to know just where it was. Sidney wondered about this, and then realized that you would expect it there near the door. On a street like this one, empty on a Sunday afternoon, it had been a mistake to leave the door ajar. Irma worried about such things, but he had told her that the burglar alarm, those silver ribbons on the window, took care of him. She believed him when he spoke of business. "Your business is business," she told him because he was proud to hear it. He had wanted the musty corners of his store to catch the summer breeze down Cousin Street, but they had been waiting; they would have figured how to get him to open the door. The Sunday stillness outside, muffled now by the locking and the curtaining, troubled him. It made no sense. "I haven't got any money with me," he said. "You can look if you want to."

"You want to write us a check?" Cash asked.

"Just make the check out to Cash," the boy at the door said, his dark lashes fluttering.

The driver, angry and jittery, wearing his cap indoors, spoke for the first time. "They don't have no check accounts. What bank'd trust a coon?" He spat against a television screen and watched with interest while the blob scuttled across the slippery, gray glass.

"I bet they got coon banks already," the short one said, looking to Cash, who did not answer him.

"Anyone asking you for money, Sid?" Cash demanded. "Don't go trying to in-gra-she-ate. Jeez, that all the light you got? Plug in some of them floor lamps, whyncha." The short man and the youth in doorman's pants did this. Yellow lights flashed on all over the store, casting bright circles among which stood the electrical appliances and the furniture which Sidney sold. "That's nice," Cash said.

"Used to live around here," the doorman said to no one in particular, "before *they* moved in. When I was a kid, I mean. Still remember the bank on the corner, the Kroger's, the candy store. Used to get that Big League gum for a penny with the pictures of Babe Ruth, Earl Averill, Joe Vosmik. They played for the Indians."

"Not Babe Ruth, he didn't," the short man said. "Bet you?" he added hopefully.

"I didn't say Ruth. Averill, Vosmik, Mel Harder, sure. Goose Goslin. No, he was for the Tigers. The place ain't changed much, least not on Sundays. Looks almost like it was."

The driver, still watching his spittle drying on the television screen, pulled at a button on his cap. "He comes here Sundays to count his money. What about you, *you* got any money to count, Cash? Let's get started."

"Now what'd I ever do with money?" Cash demanded, sad and stooping and his shoulder blades pressed like stunted wings against a faded denim shirt. He answered his own question. "Only spend it, that's all I'd ever do, friends. What do I need it for? I always lived just for the fun of it."

"Philosopher," said the doorman. "Even if it's Sunday we ain't got all day, Cash."

The little man with the newspaper jerked his head in agreement. "He told us already how he left his money in the bank, didn't you, Sid? This is his inventory day."

"I—" Sidney began.

"You," Cash said mournfully, sucking in the toothpick and shaking his head slowly.

"What do you want?" Sidney tried not to sound frightened. He hoped it would be better that way; it was better with dogs. He tried to see if he could repeat the question in the same voice, "What do you want, please?"

"We just aim to correct you, that's all, Sid," Cash said softly. "We been doing a lot of thinking. There's a white folks' business district, whyncha, and there's a coons' business district. You personally, you're too much on the edge."

"Looks a little on edge to me, too," the doorman said. His pretty, movie-usher face scowled with approval of the joke. He liked to take Cash's words and play with them.

The little man and the driver were impatient. "How about beginning the correctment?" The little man twisted his roll of newspaper until it squealed.

Sidney heard an automobile slow down on the street outside. He tried by thinking to force it to stop, to open, to send someone out curious to see a blinded window with cracks of electric light coming through. Someone might wonder about that. Maybe he hadn't thought it hard enough, because the automobile just went by. Anyway, in the quiet afternoon outside, with the sun bright on this side of the street, you would have to look carefully to catch the electricity burning. People weren't all that curious. Sidney often felt, in the kind of life he had made for himself, that he needed to think things harder in order to amount to something. Someone outside, those others, they had turned the slant of the sun hard on his storefront. The sound of tire on brick had faded.

Still they looked at him, but no one moved. Cash glanced at the telephone on the desk as if to urge him toward it. Cash picked up the frame on the desk and pocketed the raffle ticket inserted at the edge. There was a framed photograph in sepia of a woman in a flowered housedress. She was smiling. She had written something on the print under the glass. "Friend of yours?" Cash asked.

"My wife."

"Married with a license, eh? She's sort of lighter in the picture'n you," Cash observed, examining it critically. "Got a brownish kind of color, ain't she? Not black, least that's the way it looks. Nose too. What's her name, whyncha?"

"Look, I never did anything to you fellows—"

The driver moved toward him with a sigh, content to leave the sight of his spittle on a 19-inch television screen. Cash shook his head at the driver and then looked at Sidney again, repeating the question, "What's her name?" The driver shrugged angrily and stopped.

"Irma."

"Irma," said Cash.

"Irma," said the doorman approvingly. "That's okay, that's a black kind of name."

"Sounds sort of brown to me," Cash said. "No use arguing." He studied the picture, his narrow skull bent over it and the enlarged Adam's apple constricted in leathery wrinkles.

"Ain't we talking too much?" the driver asked Cash. "You can never tell what's up, almost anything."

"We don't have to hide the face or hurry ourself for any coon. You itchy somewheres, friend? Keep your gloves on."

For the first time Sidney noticed that they all wore the same pink, smooth, slippery hands. It was a look he didn't like even when Irma used them for the dishes. For the detergent, she said.

"It's awful sweaty, Cash," the driver said. "Mine's going to rip, I'm telling you."

"Just so it's only the hands sweat on us. Say, Sid, do white men all look the same to a coon? I always wanted to ask one, whyncha. You looked the same to me till I got to know you."

"Stands to reason, Cash," the short man said. "The man's in a hurry, like the driver says. Like Freddy says,"—and the short man grinned happily to inform Sidney that it didn't matter if he knew their names.

"Maybe so," Cash admitted, his sad eyes roving again toward the telephone, and the soft, purple, veiny flesh about them pulsating with an impatience only now admitted. He grinned and chewed his toothpick and enjoyed his impatience and that of his friends.

Sidney was listening for a cry, a call, a sound outside in the silence of the June-Sunday afternoon on a commercial side-street. He knew that they were waiting for him to move first and that he might as well get it over with. Their soft drawling, their impatience, their questions were only to urge him to move first. He felt oddly worried about the jittery driver, who seemed afraid of Cash, and the pasty-faced boy in the fancy trousers, who seemed driven to annoy his friend Cash with his jokes.

Cash raised the framed photograph and let it fall, the thin glass tinkling and splintering.

Poor Cash and all his responsibilities.

Because it was expected of him, Sidney lunged toward the telephone without even bothering to reach out his hands for it. Cash moved with a quick grace surprising in one so tall, lifting him with a kick in the groin. Then he flopped and lay writhing on the floor. The little fat man and the youth bent down to tie him with cord from the doorman's jacket pocket. Cash watched. Despite the sickness, Sidney felt relieved that they had begun already. He tried to lie still.

"Oh my, shouldn't have done that," the doorman said, daintily dancing out of the splash of vomit and broken glass where Sidney choked and gasped. The doorman looked longingly at all the appliances on the floor, his girlish eyes like those Sidney sometimes saw in the front seats of convertibles on Saturday night. "Let me turn things on, Cash," he pleaded. "Come on, let me." Cunningly he thought of a reason: "In case he makes a noise while you work. Let me do it, Cash."

On both sides of him like that, his feet and arms bound tight, he could not even roll away from them. While the other three bent over Sidney—three pairs of eyes in three pale colors above three fixed mouths—the doorman pranced about the store, connecting double sockets, plugging in television sets and radios and washing machines and letting their blare fill Sidney's ears. It took a long time. Yes! This meant something to him now. He heard the ball game, a voice telling how to lose weight without hunger, the roar of a vacuum cleaner. No, that sound was in his head. He had sold out his last vacuum cleaner. For awhile he could see the toothpick. Then it seemed to disappear with the face of Cash.

He wondered why there was no short circuit. Maybe because his was the only store on the block using current on Sunday. No, no, it wasn't that, he couldn't figure it anymore.

He did not know if his eyes were open. Long before they left, he had stopped seeing them. He could still hear the fins of the washing machines and driers churning, the Mixmaster mumbling, the whining static of a radio at the high on no station at all. They left the lights blazing, but closed the door carefully behind them. The telephone began to ring. It was probably Irma. The fuses still did not blow.

When the noise finally brought the police, they broke through the door and, as the burglar alarm clanged, the appliances fell into silence. The telephone was still ringing. Sidney, whose eyes remained open on his store, was no longer able to listen to the scratch of the policemen's pencils or the rumor of the June-Sunday evening outside. The fins of one sluggish wash-o-mat flapped in the dry air, but he had stopped worrying about what sense it made for him. Someone took the telephone off its hook and set it on the table. There was no hurry about the ambulance. He amounted only to what others had amounted before him.

FOUR CONTEMPORARY TURKISH POETS

DEAD

FAZIL HUSNU DAGLARCA

I want to die in a place
Where there is no imam.
I do not want anyone to see
How beautiful are my feet, my hair, my everything.

Clean and free in the name of death,
A fish in seas unknown.
Am I not a Moslem? I am!
But I do not want a crowd.

Do not disturb my darkness in the air
By wrapping me in white sheets.
And do not shake my body on your shoulders;
All of my limbs are dreaming.

No prayer can make up for the distance
Between the universes and me.
Do not wash my body! Do not!
I love my warmth frantically!

—translated by A. Turan Oflazoglu

AUDIENCE

FAZIL HUSNU DAGLARCA

I am Halim the third, magnificent and sacred,
The sultan of sultans;
From my white hands begin
The days of my subjects.

The instant I stand in
Conveys my warmth to virgins unknown.
I discover time
From my own continuity.

To my body extend
All the dimensions of the universe,
And my palaces are comfortable
With my body only.

I have freed, together with great eagles,
Science, poetry, and victory
To make the coming generations happy
Upon seas and upon lands.

The heavens are proper to my head—
Dark and blue.
My love and blood, as two infinitudes,
Are equal to each other.

As noble, beautiful, healthy, and absolute
As possible by reason,
I am Halim the third—
And who are you, O mountains and rocks?

—translated by A. Turan Oflazoglu

THOUGHTS IN A HOUSE IN A GARDEN

FAZIL HUSNU DAGLARCA

Who has deceived these people
That no one cares about death?
O death! wider than the heavens,
I have no room for you in my heart.

How, how to part with life?
It's neither a country, nor a garment.
The whole universe may perish,
But how may I cease to be?

II

Open the doors, leave your work!
And gather together in villages, in cities, in countries.
Press your thinking heads to the ground
And listen to the trees that kiss the heavens.

And sing a song toward the sky,
Making the stars and destinies hear you.
And revive, in the distance, like desires
The past days of everyone.

Mothers! smother your children!
They project your lives beyond the future.
Fathers! plaster the walls
To shut life out of the houses!

III

No! They will not hear my words,
But stare on, smiling at me.
Am I the only one, I wonder, who is living,
And the only one who shall die?

—translated by A. Turan Oflazoglu

TIME FOR THINKING

A. TURAN OFLAZOGLU

There is always time for thinking.
While sitting before the switchboard
I can always see the blue sky green,
The green boughs red.
And there are times when I decide—
I am quite serious—to nail
All the passers-by to the ground,
And free the trees, the buildings and the mountains from
    their laziness.
I command them to pillage the splendor of the stars.
Alas! They will obey.
Do they dare disturb my fancy?
O leisure time! O time for thinking.

I have told them again and yet again not to neglect me.
I have told them I might covet
Their beloved, bread on their sanctuaries,
But they would not listen.
Now I see what I must do,
I know what I can do.
Alas, they have never thought that I have been thinking
And will be thinking before the switchboard, in the streets,
    in the classrooms, in their brains!
O leisure time! O time for thinking!

THE STREETS

SAMI FERLIEL

Mother, I step into the streets
In the name of God
Upon your advice.

I see, the streets are not as they were
When I used to look out of the window.

Men were quite different,
The sky also was different, I see.
The streets lead one to so many places.

Bright and dark are the streets.
Under these circumstances, Mother,
I have acquired ever-green loves.
Night long I struggle for my loves;
Impossible, impossible to defeat me!
Thanks to God
My fists are as heavy as nature.

MY OTHER FRIEND

GUZIN YALTER

You ask me why so late,
What kept me so very late.
You ask me why so dismal,
The tears so wet, so shed.
Why the bruises, the spirit dishevelled.
Why ask?
I was with my other friend.

My never-parting,
My ever-gnawing,
Bosom friend.
Heavily lingering,
Viciously caressing,
Bountiful in pain,
Passionate in claim.

You ask me again why so late,
What kept me so very late.

Why so out of breath
As though I had been with death.

Ask not. I am with my other friend,
My dark mood, my gloomy state,
My desperate old friend.

MOSCARDINO

ENRICO PEA

translated by Ezra Pound

The Signora Pellegrina went into mourning at once, she put on black silk, put a black hem on her night-gowns, lowered the blinds, and lit a lamp on the wide linen-cupboard.

She was of high lineage and had come in for the shares of two sisters who had gone into convents and passed away early, but her husband had been a poor hand at guiding the domestic economy and had left little either of her good heritage or of his own. He had been honorary physician to the Confraternity of the Misericordia, and High Chamberlain of the Church of San Lorenzo, he had had, therefore, a magnificent funeral.

The Signora Pellegrina showed no signs of grief at his passing. She said: Well out of it; you are.

Then she assembled her three sons and called Cleofe, the general servant who had come from the mountains, to act as witness:

You are all three grown men.

Your progenitors are no longer. Divide what is left.

The clothes I have on are my own. Don't grumble if I wear silk.

After that she forgot to talk, as if turned mute.

My grandfather was the youngest of the Signora's three sons. The middle one was named Lorenzo after the town's patron saint and also because he had been born in the year that the doctor had been made High Chamberlain (or accountant) of the Church of San Lorenzo. He had been sickly from the start, didn't walk till he was five, stuttered a little, and his remarks were so peculiar that people thought he was making up fairy tales. His father had intended him for the priesthood. That was another reason for calling him Lorenzo after the saint and the church with the marble steps and stone bench against its façade, and the chairs tilted against the outer wall from where one can watch the river with the winter sun beating down on poor men's bent shoulders.

Be it said that these oldsters were lined up like culprits with a cane gripped between their knees, and that they mumble without moving their lips so that they shan't make a draft or displace the air with their thin bodies. Noon stirs them and they carry off as much sun as has sunk into them, walking quickly because the shade of the accacias is full of pitfalls for age, and the accacias, lined up before the old folk's home, throw a shade even in winter, and steal thereby that much sun from the aged.

I don't remember the eldest brother's name but he had a terror of blood, he was grumpy and ugly and watched himself perpetually in the mirror, terrified and bursting into tears at the slightest provocation.

Servants did not stay long. It was not an easy house for a servant.

The Doctor and Signora Pellegrina used to get up for mass at sunrise and for communion. The girl was expected to tell Mrs. Pellegrina not to swallow water while she was washing, she was expected to hand the doctor the gray shawl that he wore like a cape over his shoulders.

If the boys had committed a misdemeanour they were expected to confess after mass, especially if it had been of an embarrassing nature.

Grumpy had his coffee in bed. He stared up fixedly at the servant girl, from foot to head with his knees hunched up to his chest and his horse face unshaved. The girl approached him with a feeling of terror and loathing, and Grumpy continued to keep his hands under the covers as if there was nothing in front of him holding a cup. Which nothing finally said: Hurry up! Signor Padrone. Whereafter he would at leisure bring out a hairy paw like an ape's.

The abbé wandered about the house all day long with his hands in the folds of his soutane. The servant was expected to say: Don Lorenzo, take your hands out of the slits. Then Don Lorenzo sniggered; went into the kitchen, lifted the lids of the pots with the ugly hands that had been in the slits of his soutane.

In the evenings when the abbé was in bed, the girl was expected to patch up the facings.

As my grandfather could not stand the click-clak of heels at certain times of the day the girl had to walk on tip-toe. He loathed seeing the abbé slinking about like a shadow. Every now and again he would rush at him, grab his long hair, pull out a few hairs from back-centre: O.K. that's where you'll be having your tonsure. He also picked on Grumpy, but less often.

He also slapped the servant. He was a devil when he got into a temper, upset the whole house, tore the bed spreads with his teeth, and if his terrorized family locked a door on him he would jump out a window.

The servants came, and left when they got their month's wages.

Cleofe, the last of them all, came from the hills with her bundle on her head, and my grandfather opened the door for her.

Good morning, Sir. She said it with such charm, that he was moved. Cleofe blushed.

My grandfather in his bed room listened for the tap of her

heels, it seemed like a leit-motif, life in that house's monotony: click, tac!

Cleofe came from the hills by Terrinca, a place known for its beautiful women. They are long in the legs, with waists square as their shoulders. They are lean, with rather long faces, that seem perhaps a bit longer because they part their hair in the middle and coil it in two braids over their ears. They have very white skin, perhaps from the milk and flour diet. Their teeth are good, their lips full like those of young children, and their eyes are dark as the chestnut rind.

They carry baskets on their heads, old style, and take steps long as a man's. Their cheeks dimple in smiling. Cleofe was of this breed. It seemed as if no cloud had ever passed over that clear face and no tear ever had clouded her eyes.

How could she sleep hearing someone on tiptoe in the corridor, breathing hard at the key hole?

How could she have stood it long, in anxiety, her heart thumping and a lump in her throat?

Poor devil from the hills, she felt that no such high love was for her, she avoided it, tried to be hard, and felt anchored to the spot when he looked at her.

"I will go. I will go." Another day passed and my grandfather's face, imperious as a general's, was there saying: Never. You can not.

My grandfather was in pain if she went into Grumpy's bed room or when the abbé kept his hands in his soutane slits in her presence.

Don Lorenzo take your hands out of your pockets. She blushed if my grandfather was there to hear her. He saw it and trembled.

"I will pluck you like a dead capon!" He would have killed him but for Cleofe's intervention. She calmed him, patting his cheek.

Then my grandfather was taken with a mad passion and Cleofe could no longer meet his eyes without changing colour. Cleofe do you like me?

Nothing was said for the rest of that night, in that house. And yet everyone again heard the death rattle that they had heard a few days before when the doctor had got suddenly worse, and had almost sent for the confessor.

The rooms were full of ghostly population as that night when the dead man was no longer there but seemed to come through every opened door visibly, and a voice from purgatory seemed to move lamenting in the room.

And now the Signora Pellegrina hearing the creak of Cleofe's door was terrified as she had been *that* night. And rattled her rosary and kept listening as if he had come back from purgatory and was asking relief for his soul.

Grumpy sat with his eyes popping out the whole night, with his knees bunched up to his chest, in a bloody vision. He saw the war of '48 and the Austrian armies marching through the city, a high tide of fire, the forest moving, women disemboweled, children trodden into the mud by the horses with barbarian riders and the deafening noise of steel weapons.

Monstrous tale, my grandfather had told on his return.

He saw him in uniform, at 18, my grandfather who had planted the liberty tree in the town square, who had run away, who had gone venturing over the world, who had forded rivers, endured marches, killed enemies, plunging a bayonet into their kidneys.

My grandfather had upset an Austrian catafalque and slept in the dead man's coffin.

My grandfather scared him, made him tremble, made the house shake; what would he do now to the servant, to his mother, to Grumpy himself, to the abbé?

The abbé perambulated up and down in the corridor. Stopped at Cleofe's door, stayed fixed like a shadow with his hands in his pockets, with his head between the door and the door-frame.

The women of Terrina go to bed as God made 'em, naked.

Our house had no curtains, and the rooms are not dark at night. Don Lorenzo saw her naked, white, white, with her legs long. My grandfather seemed like a monster crouched over her, clamped to her belly, looking into her eyes.

The abbé stood there till the dead came to life, ill augured witness of my mother's procreation.

Cleofe, do you like me?

A' you? replied Cleofe bashfully as if asking it of herself, Do you like me?

That was after she got over her terror, and she had not cried out, feeling resistance was useless, and even if she had wanted to, had not the strength to cry out. Love had pinned down her arms, annulled and made useless the strength of her strong body. Her breath so caught in her lungs that she had no breath, and could make no movement of denial.

Cleofe found herself in his arms as a bird willingly in the mouth of a serpent, forgetting its possession of wings. Neither wanted to weep nor could help it.

Cleofe, do you like me?

A' you?

He was calm now, and looked into her tobacco-coloured eyes, held her head firm with his two hands on her cheeks and felt the blood beat in her temples, felt it in the pads of his finger tips, felt the warm breath coming from Cleofe's mouth that his hands distorted. Cleofe had the sea's tempest in her ears, felt the wind bringing winter now, over the house roof, in the tops of the trees that guard it.

In the court-yard was the well-curb with twisted iron work over it, and the stone edge gone mossy, the cord looped over a hook, the well-bucket hooped with iron shrunk on as a wheel-rim.

The well went a hundred yards down. Town perched on a mountain, the well, bored through clay and rock, narrow and crooked, down, down, through the cracks, through the tufts of nettle and pellatory.

When they drew water, the pulley wheel turned: Chio, kao, kao. The drops of the well bucket, coming up jerkily, echoed the clink.

Grumpy stopped his ears because the *gi-gi* of the pulley

set his teeth on edge as sour lemon or when he heard pumice scraped on the marble sink. But since he was now domiciled in the court yard he was drawn on by curiosity to look into the well, drawn by the clear clink of the pulley that was like a bell struck by the subterranean spirits, so, little by little, with one ear, then with both he could stand hearing the turn of the pulley without feeling goose-flesh.

He looked down the well trembling and saw only darkness, not even water which the spirits had covered with lead, with a cloud-coloured mantle that was passing over the sky.

Grumpy thought he saw a river churning down there at the well-bottom, and thought he could hear a noise like that of the mill-race when the motive wheel moves in a saw mill. But he saw only a slab of lead and heard only the wandering of his own voice losing itself in the void beneath him.

When he grew bolder he threw stones into the well and saw circles shake on the water and saw his face in frightened reflection, deformed and recomposed in the whirlpool, submerged in the ripples as little by little the spirits restrained the water under their leaden mantles.

He began to take his meals on the green well-curb, casting a glance now and then into the deep at the swarming of shadows heaped like clouds, but smaller, a comic dwarf leaning there on his elbows the better to hide.

And he began to wind the well cord over the hook and the well crane, a hundred yards of it, bendable but shriveled stiff like a steel wire.

Grumpy made a regular skein round and united as the circles of the well water, smiling now and again. Thus he learned to look pleasant.

The abbé preferred to dawdle about under the orange trees which were also there in the court yard aligned at the far end, clipped low so that the branches should not spread over the wall. If he looked down the well it made him dizzy, things swam before his eyes, he got pinwheels as when he

shut them facing the sun to see lights and glows of many
colours.

There were the stubs of column, also, on which the old
people had set the broken tubs from Montelupo that the
tinker had patched up with wire and lumps of plaster, so
that they now held earth as well as they had once held the
washing. The old tubs from Montelupo with two masks and
mottoes:

"Like to like."

"God makes 'em, and then gives 'em mates they deserve."
Now they were full of rich earth, geraniums and daisies
green in them so as to look like a shrub trunk with small
flowers round it not passing the edge. Grumpy drew up the
water, the abbé carried it to the old jars from Montelupo.
They were painted now to conceal their age, the cracks, the
snubbed noses of the masks, covered with a sort of red chalk
that you use to paint tiles in a bed-room. Thus when the
abbé had drowned the flowers that didn't pass the tub's edge
there was a bloody wreathe round the tubs.

Grumpy wouldn't come near them for fear of that spilled
blood on the ground, and the abbé never looked down the
well for fear of dizziness.

That was their way of passing the time, as it was now
impossible for them to stay indoors. My grandfather watched
Grumpy's eyes, and the abbé's hands stuffed through the un-
faced slits of his soutane.

If Grumpy so much as looked at Cleofe, dinner was off.

Grumpy barricaded himself in his room and the abbé had
no hair left where his tonsure should have been, it was now
twice the size of most priest's; and Cleofe could no longer
keep my grandfather calm. Her gentleness only drove him
wild and made him crazy with jealousy.

"Your brother will kill you one day." And Grumpy shut his
eyes and saw my grandfather in uniform with his eyes shining scarlet.

And "that woman's" sweetish voice crept into his ears,

trembling as if with compassion, almost as if she were weeping, there were tears almost in her voice full of urgence.

Grumpy no longer had his mother to fondle him. Threats at his throat if he so much as cast an affectionate glance, he crept into the house like a sneak thief, felt like a burglar if caught, barricaded himself in his room to keep from being flayed alive; and "that woman" who came so often to the well, did she know it? Did she know, and was she afraid he would die soon?

She was perhaps his guardian angel that had watched over his childhood. A great wave of feeling swept over her that she could express only with her eyes closed, weeping: Your brother will kill you one of these days.

Grumpy shut his eyes: And you, Don Lorenzo, do you remember your mother, before she went off her head? Nobody would touch a hair of your head then.

And Don Lorenzo sniggered, as he did when Cleofe looked at him.

Grumpy was drawing up water, and that woman stood with her thighs close to him as if wanting to help him.

When the bucket was in reach she leant over the well-curb to take it, crushing her belly against the green stone so that her thighs seemed to hold up two antennae as the wooden braces hold up the country-side bridges.

Her breast lay heavy almost falling out of her linen dress gathered in at the neck like the tunic of a Madonna.

Grumpy looked at the freckles on her breasts; so near now he could see her heart-throbs. Her throat brushed his hand and he shut his eyes as if in terror, and if the odor of lavender, released from the folds of the linen blouse puffed out by the weight of her breasts, reached into his nostrils he closed his eyes terrified with his legs weak as if in a fit of malaria.

So they remained hung over the well-curb in abandon, Grumpy's head drawn like a weight toward the well bottom among the shadowy spirits which took hold of the bushy hair of the reflected head and beat it against the head of the woman reflected, so that the images were melted together, one over the other, striking and melting together.

Now her mouth was against his ear saying strange words, dizziness in his soul as in the ripples on the water beneath him.

Grumpy remained stock still with his eyes closed, he felt her mouth move away from his ear and fastened to his nape; a circle of fire, a brand to leave lasting mark.

But Cleofe who had brought her milky and blood-tinted face from the mountains now had circles under her eyes and there was a waxen shadow on her clear face. The dark spots that had showed her pregnant had not left with the birth.

Her mouth was no longer cool, her lips were thin now. Only her eyes seemed larger.

Perhaps her thought ran: If I had married a shepherd in my own mountains, now I would be happy. She wept in the day time, lamenting that she had not enough milk, as have the women of her own village, they have it so that they suckle the lambs. That is abundance.

If she had married a shepherd she would be free, all that milk, all those sons, all that sky and a will to singing. . . .

And now instead, she was afraid of the man who was her husband in that shadowy house.

Why do you look at yourself in the glass?

You have combed your hair to look prettier.

Why do you want to look prettier?

If someone went by in the street, if anyone stood near a window in one of the neighboring houses, if someone knocked at the door to collect a bill or bring a message, there was a bloody row.

Everything was in turmoil and chaos in my grandfather's mind.

Cleofe did not answer, ever. She obeyed, she looked terrified. Her face was full of suspicion, like that of my grandfather's, unquiet.

He wanted her not to wash, so that she would be ugly; to leave her hair uncombed, to wear the country clothes that she had brought with her, out of date, of gray flannel, plow-man's shoes, canvas aprons, fichus crossed on her breast.

That she should look badly, that she should dress like an old woman so that no one would look at her.

And even so my grandfather found her more beautiful, too beautiful. It was the majesty of her figure; unsuppressible by the clumsiness of old-fashioned clothes. Taking from her the grace of fashion, her beauty shone through as a joke, almost as a dream, as if she were a girl of past time.

Sometimes he wanted to feel he was right, tortured him-self, helping her to put on her good clothes.

A new dress of shot silk, with a white front and a low lace collar.

He wanted her to put on the necklace of gold beads with a cross, and with her hair coiled round her cheeks and ears as when she had come down from the hills. Then he watched her move away, his eyes fixed on her as if in a vision, as something no longer his.

He wanted her to stand on the balcony so that the sun-light could play over her dress, so the gold beads could come to life, so that her face would seem again compound of milk and blood.

He forced himself to indifference before the serenity of that wax Madonna, lept as it were of a sudden from among the rays of god to his balcony.

But if anyone passed and turned unexpectedly, if a shadow showed at a window of an house opposite, the spell broke and his being was shattered, trembling, brute jealousy lept back with all its instincts, he slammed shut the window to shut out the sun's kindness, he tore the gold beads from Cleofe's neck, trampled them, tore the shot silk dress to tatters, tore it with his teeth, stripped it off her.

Cleofe grew worse.

The doctor came to the house and my grandfather had a new war within him, everything in him on fire, so that if he concealed his anguish it shone terribly through his eyes.

Cleofe wanted to get well again.

And the doctor's presence increased my grandfather's torment, drop by drop, a whirling torrent, that Cleofe felt with terror.

The doctor had looked at her breasts, had felt her belly, pressed his head between her shoulders to listen, and tapped her white body all over. Cleofe felt it would drive my grandfather off his head. She wanted all the while to get well.

Her heart beat so hard, her legs trembled, now and again she felt a wave of heat pass over her face.

She wanted at all costs to get well.

She got up too soon. It was mid September, a month of nostalgia for Cleofe, busy time in the mountains, getting ready the logs for the chestnut drying, they would smoke early this year as it had hardly rained all the summer.

The chestnuts were beginning to ripen in their burrs. The burrs had grown big, the nuts were full and meaty. They'll be smoking 'em early this year.

She stood by the window. Below was an arbour with ripe grapes hanging to the lattices. The arbour stripped of leaves with the wire braces, with the fronds and tendrils still branching, the dead branches bent with the weight of the grape clusters, the shoots sticking out at the top with unopened butts.

A September already cold, though fanned with scirocco, a few reddish clouds, rain's sheeplets feeding in grassless meadow.

Heaven calm, but unlit, a grey dampness pervading the house and a will to let the eyes close.

My grandfather held her up, by the balustrade and she looked down into the court yard or gazed at the light gallop of far clouds going mountainward.

The square orange flowers that had given fragrance in spring time were now dark balls in the lighter leaves.

In the tubs from Montelupo the small flowers were drowned, the water sloshing to the brim was tinted with the red cinnabar brick paint. My grandfather drew her from the balcony into his arms, put his palms against her shoulders, rubbed the backs of her hands, stroked down her arms, her flanks, her legs, down to her feet, and lamented: Cleofe, you are too lovely, you are what is driving me mad, my despair, lifelong despair. Cleofe, I shall have no peace I shall have no peace as long as you are alive . . . and I am alive. Cleofe, death is good. Death is good.

Cleofe repeated: death, and turned her eyes away, and toward the child in its cradle; which, awakened by the noise, kicked and screamed. To die. My grandfather had a knife in his hands. Cleofe, I can't kill you.

He fell on the knife, slitting his belly.

The first person to reach the door was "that woman," who had kissed Grumpy by the well curb.

Then the doctors who put my grandpa in a straight waistcoat and sewed up his stomach.

He was off his head and didn't notice he was being carried away.

When Sabina, the woman who had kissed Grumpy at the well curb, came in and saw my grandfather with his stomach slit, twitching on the ground, she ran to call her padrone, Don Pietro, Pietro Galanti who lived next us and whose house had two doors, one on the tiled street and the other giving onto the court yard toward the well. The abbé Don Lorenzo walked behind Sabina bobbing along to catch up. He went up Don P.G.'s stairs while she was calling the priest, he fetched out the silver crucifix and the stole and the surplice and the box with the holy objects that was in the downstairs cupboard.

It was not the first time he had scurried to death beds with Don Pietro Galanti and these were the things necessary on such occasions.

Then he fixed Don Galanti's tunic from behind and helped him to get on with the job as if it were perfectly ordinary and in no way alarming even if the slit stomach belonged to his brother.

Don Lorenzo stood still before Cleofe, smiled, stared at her quite a while with his hands in the folds of his soutane, quite calmly. Now, at any rate the disemboweled was in the

hands of all those doctors and could no longer jump on him
and tweek the hairs out of his tonsure as he had done in
times past.

If you want to see your brother before they take him away
. . . He may die . . . up on that mountain near Lucca . . .
tied up the way they have got him . . . all that way on a
stretcher . . . Signora Pellegrina, I wouldn't like my pre-
sentiment to come true . . . wouldn't it be better for him to
die here at home . . . at least he would go to the cemetery
where his father . . . and where we all, anyhow.

Signora Pellegrina, you might at least say something or
other to keep 'em from taking him away. . . . You are his
mother, I have done every . . . I have told 'em to let him
die in peace in his bed.

There was a pool of blood on the floor.

How can a man live without blood? It's true, it's all god's
will, but god's will could cure him in his own bed.

To die in his own bed. . . .

The mayor says it can't be done.

I haven't been able even to give him the sacraments.

The Misericordia will be here . . . anyhow it's your business . . . come see him before they take him away and give
him your benediction before they get him out of the door.

Mrs. Pellegrina trembled and stared into nothingness,
rolled her eyes from the depth of her armchair . . . and
didn't answer.

Her teeth clicked from time to time, and the beads of the
rosary tapped one against another. And a fugg in that room
that hadn't been opened for months, a smell of oil wick and
of mould, a feeling of death. That skeleton hardly moved by
its trembling . . . hunched into wide sided arm chair in the
darkness of the room.

When the Misericordia did come with the coffin and the
two horses the whole village was on the brick sidewalk.

Toward evening. Cloudlets reddish and dark, hurrying in
escape, in herds, from sea to hills. Those far off seemed like

one cloud thinned out on a turquoise sky, more blackish than reddish.

The cold breeze stung the women's faces and they stopped their mouths with their yarn tippets keeping their hands under their aprons so that their bellies seemed to bulge out. They stood stock still looking at our house, close to the opposite wall like a frightened flock of pregnant and widowed witches.

Those two horses with traces and harness ends of yellow leather, brass buckles, bridles with square blinkers that almost boxed in the horses' noses to keep them from shying, and with tinklers on their heads to keep them from going to sleep, bits with two small bars of iron sticking out on each side of their mouths, from which the rope reins passed over their rumps between two oval rings set in the tiny saddle atop the belly-band, rings oval shaped like old fashioned key tops.

One sorrel and one chestnut with their knees bundled in cloth, their tails bundled up, with their ears twitching against the shiny blinkers, that man with the embroidered hat with the four reins between the fingers of his heavy hands, high up, above the horses, with his whip-end touching the ground and the covering of the catafalque trailing behind, covered with oil cloth like an uneven warming pan; a terrifying apparition never described in the book of fears.

Meanwhile it was getting dark and this mechanism started toward the Lucca asylum down the steep brick-paved lane, the creaking breaks slowed the wheels . . . chi-chi-chieee . . . wailing of wounded crows in the tragic evening.

A window was thrown open and a living skeleton appeared. A howl and thud. The pregnant witches took their hands out from under their aprons as if to deliver themselves from an evil.

Mrs. Pellegrina had fallen on her back. Broken her skull, could not be given the sacraments.

Everybody in this damned house dies without being given the sacraments.

I adore thee in every instant, O living bread of heaven, O sacrament of the most high.

Tomorrow thou shalt be with God.

Say: Jesus, Joseph, Mary.

But the eyes were set and glassy. Don Pietro had held a lighted candle to her lips and the flame does not waver.

Sabina, tie a handkerchief under her chin so her mouth won't flop open.

The rosary is in her hand.

She is dressed in black silk, all you need do is to light another lamp and keep watch.

Grumpy still had that pool of blood before his eyes, and his head now wrapped in a woolen shawl.

He looked in the mirror but did not recognize himself, he has seen the bare skull of death inside his face.

He has opened his mouth to count his teeth feeling they will drop out of his violet coloured gums one by one before long.

He has wrapped his head in the shawl to keep out sound, to keep out visions. But the dancing lights suddenly swelled, exploded. Fire, fire, they were burning into his brain and he could not open his eyes.

He heard that woman's voice in his ears, a gust of warm breath on his neck, her mouth as that day at the well . . . and a going and coming through the house.

Tomorrow thou shalt be with God.

He no more knew which throbbed worse, skull, heart or head, it seemed as if a wind were tearing the shawl from his shoulders.

A gust of wind, like a gust of wind, he felt two hands clutching his wrists, violently holding . . .

and that woman's voice . . .

Perhaps it is a snare of the devil, and the wind is blowing. . . .

Tomorrow thou shalt be with God. Jesus, Mary, Joseph another fire burst amid the bright dancing spots.

and the wind pulling his shawl. His head was stunned, it gurgled, flopped, thick and foamy as if the picked bones of his skull were full of red wine-must.

Death was helping the wind tear his clothes off, must he flee naked?

They would think he was mad, like his brother. . . . They would take him to the Lucca asylum, like his brother . . .

And another blood-puddle.

Now they have put a cold shirt on him, they are laying him out in his coffin, they are covering him with a linen sheet, cold, rough, dampish, as when you get into bed in winter after long weeks of wind off the North Mountain, where the sun never comes for three months at a time, and the caves are full of icicles dripping.

His legs ache. He will never be warm again.

Jesus, Joseph, Mary, O living bread of Heaven.

The voice of that woman attacked him, a warm gust of wind on his neck. He seemed to feel her mouth now on one ear, now on the other. He no longer sees red.

That woman has squirted drops of ink into his eyes, she has sucked out the beast that was gurgling inside him, there in his head that is now black and empty.

It is night now, the baby stops whimpering, Cleofe is rocking it; rock, beat, double tap the legs of the straw woven chair on the tiled floor with a dull tap.

Cleofe looked like the Mater Dolorosa with the child Jesus. Resigned, pallid, unweeping. Unwrapped the child which stopped whimpering.

The night leaned its hairy stomach against the windows, the panes were warm and opaque, beaded with sweat. The window frames showed white, and the divisions between the glass squares. Outside all black, everything black in the room. A single candle is not much to light a whole room. The blackness hides behind pieces of furniture and bulges out round the sides. The bed has leant its shore on the floor tiling, a wedge-shaped shadow which shows exaggeratedly wide and odd.

It is mussed with the mattresses rolled to the top, the green and red stripes are like furrows at night in a mountain field.

Sugar is being burnt in a pan, the air feels viscous and sticky. The smoke passes in front of the mirror of the wardrobe and seems as if it would go on a long way into the darkness. They have washed up the blood spots with salt and water. The candle ogles, flickers onto the damp still remaining there, there is a huge patch between the bed and the window as if someone had dropped a wine flask.

Cleofe's shadow appears and disappears on the wall with the child at breast. Were it still you would say it melted into the paleness of the wall so vague that it seems but to continue the things about it.

Greyness, rain without clatter.

The sky is hooded over as far as the sea, seemed held up like a canopy by the mountains that edge the horn of Seravezza.

The tapers of the Misericordia crowd in along the walk that is paved with thin bricks, a thick cloud of smoke a bit above hooded heads.

When they had got the coffin onto their shoulders, it looked like a burning bier on four pillars, black pillars, quenched with the rain and suffocated with a dark brown cloth with metal corn tassels at the four supports almost unraveled in yellow.

The coffin moved thus down the steep lane, and behind it Don Lorenzo bareheaded, and the women with the brass lanthorns. The smoke of the torches hung in the air, tarnished the window panes, crept into the house, sticky, resinous, heavy.

Don Lorenzo is now in front of the coffin and stares at his mother in her silk dress, with her hands crossed on her breast, shackled by justice forever, her head bound, her mouth closed, one eye just a bit open.

They lift her from the litter by cords.

She is stiff.

They box her up like a bit of merchandise, put a double turn of rope round the casket and lower her into the grave as into a ship's hold.

The ropes are pulled up. They must be used again. They scrape against the rim of the casket with a dull sound of fraying, like pulleys of a crane.

Don Lorenzo's shoes were laced crooked with twine with mud on the ends at the low knot, and caked round the edge of his soutane, black stockings and silver buckles. He felt the water dripping down his sides from his hair, his face wet with rain and tears.

The hole swallowed back the loose earth. It looks as if yeast were swelling it up; puffing it over the edges of a garden flowered with paper, cotton and wire.

Don Pietro Galanti, family guardian, took possession of the estate. A vineyard on Ripa Hill, two bits of wood at Giustagnana, a spur of hill whose sub-soil contained an hidden vein of marble, graded "White P." the hope of the family.

The surface was rented to a charcoal burner for the time being. Four houses at Seravezza, an olive yard and a field at Bonazzera, three olive yards at Pozzi, four farms at Cugnia di Querceta, two poplar plantations, a grain plantation and seven meadows at Puntone, Stroscia, Ranocchiaio, and Cinquale.

A life allowance of four hundred dollars (*scudi*) a year to a "legitimate son who takes holy orders."

Inventory of furniture, kitchen copper and household linen.

All entrusted to Sabina, Don Pietro's servant who is surety for her and keeps the keys of the house.

Grumpy got better. Sleeps now and again with Sabina.

Cleofe weaned the baby, anointing her teats with bitter aloe.

Don Pietro was deaf, he was 71 with a few smoothe grey hairs more or less oily that hung over his ears and straggled over his low forehead with three serpentine wrinkles scarcely showing in his thin olive hide.

Prolix by nature, nobby of nose he shaved his dry face daily. On Fridays he distributed alms to the poor of his parish lined up according to the sexes right and left before his front door on the side toward the mountain where the sun never comes in winter.

Not far from the house the mountain sweats; smoothe grottoes cut in under the cliff with fungus-covered crevices, the sweat freezes with incredible icicles at its edge, exuded tears formed into glass work, as if the high altar were inverted by conjury candles without flamelets but lit from inside with prodigious transparency.

If a few wooden goats had climbed onto those blackish cavities, a shepherd with a crook and a brigand's hat it would have made a grottoed presepio to be boxed in behind glass.

Not until April when the rain is tepid and the hollow under the cliff is warmed by the sprouting moss and by other delights of God invisible to us do the fantastic candles wholly drop off and the shadows cease to play in magic luminosity.

In April after the brief rains, the sky clears, the incredible glass work melts from the hills, carrying rotten leaves with it, the grottoes are washed and retinted. The pebbles of the walks are yellowed with mud, the feet of the poor therewith splashed. The rope sandals have lost their heels and the soles worn to a frazzle from being used all the winter.

Don Pietro Galanti considered his poor, saw them as souls in purgatory that see God and remain in torment, half in joy half in sorrow.

Don Pietro's poor have their feet in the mud and wait to be un-famished by providence, the sky is clear and nightingales making new nests, the peach trees reflower and the orange trees in the gardens of the rich are pearled with new white blossoms.

Don P.G. opened his door at ten a.m. every Friday. He pauses a moment on the threshold to make quite sure there are no infiltrations of poor from outside his parish limits.

Then he emerges with his cloth purse containing the chicken feed.

The men lift their hats, the women stretch out their hands, "God reward you in paradise" was the usual verbal manifestation of gratitude, when not augmented by other explanations, excuses, after the admonitions inseparable from the eleemosinary act.

Don P.G.'s gabble annoyed the women particularly and he

was specially and nauseously longwinded with widows. He required peculiar religious observance and exemplary conduct from widows.

On Sunday Don Pietro said the ten o'clock mass and his poor flocked to the balustrade, otherwise no hand-out the following Friday.

He came slowly out of the sacristy so as to have time to count his poor. The altar boy meanwhile put the missal on the reading stand, set out the cruets of water and wine, and stood patiently at the foot of the altar steps chewing over joyously the next week's freedom consoling himself with the idea that the next week's longwindedness would fall on the junior clerk his companion.

Ten o'clock mass in San Lorenzo at the altar of the warrior saint Discoglius lasted an hour, invariably. That is until the start of the other mass said by Don Caesar the other thin priest. Don Pietro's opposite in temperament and in habits.

Don Caesar sang out of tune, had no manners, loose-jointed as the sandy cat from the nun's pharmacy, he loped up the altar steps, his head moving on springs, his hooded eyes blinking against the candle light trying to find the rubrics in the missal, in fact rather like the royal black bird in the Piazza butcher shop, pecking at the raw tripe which its owner stuffed through the wire bars of its cage.

Don Caesar thin, tobacco stained, choleric, bungling, liberal, untidy, boosy, impatient at the door of the sacristy, his legs nervous, and tapping his heels on the stone step near the bell tower, with his eye glued on the altar of the warrior saint Discoglius, awaited for Don P.G. to get to the Salveregina and leave room at the altar.

The little bell for Don Caesar's mass broke in without manners on the opening words of Don P.G.'s Salveregina, and shocked the sensibilities of Don Pietro who despite his deafness always heard the bell and felt as if it were a set of rude words addressed to him personally, and thought within himself of blasphemy and the sin of him who approacheth the altar fasting but with his heart full of wrath and presumption.

They passed midway before the High Altar, one with his

eyes sparkling with hurry, the other lowering his so as not to look at him, and seeming to nod to each other as they both bent head and knee before the sacrament of the Most High.

Don Lorenzo, the abbé, was not an ordained priest and did not come in for the annuity.

He had been to the seminary before his father's death but had forgotten whatever scraps of latin had been poked into his block. He had even forgotten the Paternoster and the Salveregina and when he served at mass he mumbled at random clucking in his throat like the women of the people when they try to join in the latin litany.

He had been thrown out of the seminary for keeping his hands in the slits of his soutane. Up till then his father had been supplicant, had begged the Archbishop time and again to find some way to consecrate him so that he could get the annuity, after which he promised to shut him up in a monastery so that with patience and god's will he might then get a little sense and education.

If his father had lived he would have fixed it one way or another; he would have taught him to read the missal by ear and from memory; he would have had him anointed priest so that he could get the annuity.

Instead of which, he had been left to himself in the court yard, under the orange trees, to count the buckets of water which Don P.G.'s servant pulled up to water the tubs from Montelupo, and finally forgot the inscriptions on them and the conception of the bottoms of his pockets; forgot that pockets have bottoms.

Don Pietro Galanti had to restart with the first exercises. He kept the house key and watched him by night. Lorenzo was put on rigid abbé's regime "rules for ecclesiastics" as Don Pietro called it, and had so impressed the abbé with this set of rules for ecclesiastics that he now kept his eyes on the clock for lessons and meals.

The house, watched by Don Pietro, took on new aspect. The abbé occasionally went to Cleofe's room, she was half the time in bed, half in the arm-chair. But he no longer smiled at her or kept his hands in his pockets; he stood mute and looked at her in terror as if my grandfather's shadow might at any instant appear.

Sometimes when Cleofe slept he was moved to tears, thinking of his mother nailed inside that box under the ground.

He felt Cleofe's death coming, because her breath came so gently, her eyes were sunk, her pallor.

Cleofe seeing him at her bedside so often and so changed, showed a maternal tenderness for him.

He blushed, began to shake again, and looked toward the door.

He felt a new attraction toward Cleofe, and thanks to this feeling he tried to look different. He had a sense of well-being, of self-respect, a sense of being alive, a sense of life, now, a bit late, just as he had learned to walk late.

He now seemed to see clear inside himself, he had new feelings never known before now. Setting his eyes forward toward death he seemed to see the limits of life, . . . opening an unknown world, a hidden treasure.

Now he could even shed tears, not for his bodily aches and pains but for his soul in torment. So that, still seeing his mother's coffin being lowered into the grave, he was moved by Cleofe's lips sketching a smile for him.

What is life anyway; if it be not softened by such tenderness for one another?

To feel that someone cares, as your own mother had, after your mother has gone under the earth.

To feel the desire to clasp the person loved, until she can no longer breathe, to be wholly united with her body. To take something eternal from her lips which can not be said with words. There it is. One could be happy in this world if the devil didn't take up arms against you.

He crossed himself, so that the devil shouldn't appear and blot out his reason.

Before summer came, the doctor ordered sea air for Cleofe during the spring and part of July . . . because she had suffered so much, passed a horrible winter always shut in her bed room.

The days began to lengthen and Cleofe had been getting up for several weeks. She coughed less; but if she went down into the garden and walked up the stairs afterward she was weighed down with enervating weakness as if she had climbed a mountain. She broke into light sweat toward nightfall, her cheeks got red and at once a light sleep like a slight torpor obliged her to close her eyes and she would stay in a doze for hours.

It had been a stiff winter, the grottoes, the river's high banks, the ravines had been constantly frozen. The water in the ravines and rivers could be seen working along with difficulty under a thick plate of ice, seeming to suffer from want of air.

It must have been gurgling loudly, whirling strongly, because it shot up at the edge of the ice all foamy. The branches, thistles, dry leaves borne along in the torrents had been caught fast in the freeze, imprisoned as if asleep, like birds in a cage of water.

The wheels of the saw mills were ringed with short thick candles of ice, with filaments and drops like pin-wheels for the Madonna del Carmine, curious boughs and branchings were formed in the river beds as if half sculptor's fine marble, half mottle in the rough stone ways gouging the bottom. Even the horse terds and cow droppings were made fantastic and precious between the icy mud of the cart tracks.

So after the feast of St. Discoglio, new varnished by old Ciampino who was also church upholsterer and decorator, there reappeared after many years the fine old *giardinera* wagon, six seater all new black and yellow with the curtains of heavy linen fringed with blue.

Grumpy was bundled up, cocoon'd with a grey shawl round his neck, such as his father had used, more grouchy he had aged so much in so short a time that many people seeing him staggering into the wagon thought of his dad, not merely because of the shawl but from facial resemblance.

He stood beside Sabina who was in her new clothes with circular ear-rings and with a pink handkerchief over her head stuck on with a gold pin that looked like a nail rammed through the nape of her neck. Her face blazing, gesticulating and rolling her eyes and her hips shaking with the wobbling of the wagon. Vibrating with full contentment she alone in that vehicle felt, and was, boss, brazen, proud of feeling that she was the real boss of a six-seater with sky-blue cushions covered with ticking that could carry so many people.

In town clothes the family doctor, bachelor, red skinned, sat opposite Don Pietro Galanti who shot knifed glances stealthily at him when turning a leaf of his breviary.

Cleofe had the lowered curtain behind her serving as support and cushion to what was left of her saddened body.

And the abbé Don Lorenzo next her with his little shiny eyes, tickled the baby's neck as it sat in Cleofe's lap.

Sabina and the red doctor were the live animals in that funeral coach. Their thought was clear, concealed by nothing save the convention of the moment. She burning with the exuberance of healthy vitality, he a man of scant learning and no scruples whatever.

Their carnal eagerness was of a certainty visible to everyone. The others moused round the same question, of flesh in heat, with tortuous imagination, and turned in on themselves in their uneasiness.

Cleofe had her eyes on the frosted hills, on the olives shot with sunlight, which fled under her gaze as she was carried from them. She let herself be borne along as in a dream without thinking, as a soul in transmigration, as if her life were ending, gently, in beatitude, and the child which as yet had neither reason nor soul, slept cradled.

The red poppies amid the grain flashed into Grumpy's eyes. The red head of the medico jutted out like a flashing ball of copper, speckled now and again by rays of sun at play in the branches. Dizziness, dazzle, those splotches of sun lept from the doctor's red poll onto Grumpy's hands and played over them, and onto his grey shawl, his face, and bit into him with a voluptuous malignity.

Grumpy felt the pain almost on the surface of his skin. He had been feeling pain ever since the doctor had asked to go with them and use the sixth free seat in the carry-all.

But as they went along this painful sensation grew more and more unbearable till he had to scratch his hands now and again as if stung by an insect, and tap his face now and again. He had to keep from looking at the doctor's head because he always met the watchful eyes so near him . . . as if they were right to strip Sabina stark naked.

And as they went along and along the doctor's eyes (Jack of Clubs) knew more and more about Sabina's legs, now that her dress losing its laundered stiffness, stuck to them, now that there was a hollow between leg and leg made by the weight of Sabina's hands resting there.

And how would Grumpy have the courage to say a word of reproof to the doctor who could give him a powder of something and kill him off like a dog if he needed the doc for a constipation?

He worried: That doctor will come every day as he has done for two years. . . .

And is today the first time? . . . and he convinced himself that the doctor had come to an agreement with Sabina, they had cooked up this trip to the seaside between 'em.

Jack of Clubs had arranged with her that he would be waiting by the new bridge under the plane trees.

Why had she told the driver to go by the New Bridge and not by the Annunziata?

Was it Sabina who told him? Cleofe's need of sea air had been invented on purpose?

This had all happened because of Cleofe. He hoped she would die soon and end it. That confounded consumptive, would hang on for a long time yet, he would have to stand it or die off himself.

He scratched his head, his hands, got up, hitched the shawl round his neck, looked at Don Pietro Galanti with begging eyes. Turned his eyes to the fields, there were the red poppies. He looked at Cleofe, there was that damn one-lunger, cause of it all; who might at least die off and end it, then the doctor wouldn't come to the house any more. He didn't know where to look, if he cast his gaze inward he was terrified. He remembered all his past life, the meeting at the well, the first fear of those mocking reflections down in the water beneath him; which took him by the hair and slapped him against Sabina's face, that was the first bewitchment, hoodoo. Then that woman kissed him. That brought the blood of his disemboweled brother back before his eyes.

He saw red for the rest of the drive.

Gulls at rest on the sea-water, in little groups, crowds of them further off, others scattered over a sea fanned by a cool north west wind. Patternless as a field of daisies sprouting in an unbounded meadow.

A sea paler than spring grass feathered by so gentle a breeze, petals blown off, deflowered.

A sea streaked by little furrows, unpatterned as soon as formed, as if a golden comb passed invisible, lining the white and blue, a page of the book eternally fabulous upsetting all men's calculations.

On the hard beach inshore the water scarcely moved, without foam, as if the sea breathed in blessed rest. No shadow of effort in the sleeping giant.

Cleofe hunched up on the sand under a black umbrella, not much shade, but enough for her. She does not feel the sun's heat though the sun is already high.

With all the pale sea in her eyes, sinuosity of the gulls, small pigeons new hatched, black and white with their wings open on the live water. Great lake as a bed for water lilies, amazed at the soon come summer.

Tota pulchra es. Wholly fair art thou, Mary full of Grace! The abbé Don Lorenzo was reading the book of Sunday prayers for the month of May the most amorous pages that the faithful can say to the Virgin when she stands in the silver niche unveiled for the evening novena, with the golden rosebuds and the celestial mantle and on her rosy forehead the crown of lilies which shines and shakes to the echo of children's voices.

Wholly fair art thou, Mary, piena di grazia said the abbé in a tiny lowered voice in the shadow near Cleofe.

It was the first time he had been so near that Madonna, who seemed to breathe, absorbed, with all the gleaming sea reflected in her tobacco coloured eyes.

That pale wax face, the head bent toward the left shoulder, protected from the sun rays by a black baldacchino, with the child at breast as Mary in the desert of Egypt, followed by Herod. Eyes the colour of Macaboy snuff.

Full of grace; wholly fair art thou; Mary; for the first time Don Lorenzo dared to speak so near to her, protected by the shadow of the little black rain umbrella.

Tota pulchra es, Mary, piena di grazia. He spoke the words of the Christian poet, and though protected by the shadow he was not free, he felt his heart caught in his throat and coughed every now and again a dry nervous cough.

He laboured and mistook the words, and the accents of the prayers which he would have liked to sing out in a song for her, to her, who watched the sea and listened to the break of the wavelets like the rustling of starched petticoats.

Don Lorenzo's words were heard, perhaps, and carried away by the angels who form the crown of mortal praises about Maria Regina. They were absorbed in space as if they had not been uttered aloud.

And in all the circumambience there was a divine and placid agitation of love, a submissive labour, a weeping without sobs, a smiling without disturbance of men, or of things, a calm striving.

The men scratching for mussels in shore with iron pincers stood like the gold hunters in the dime novels silently prying off shell fish amid the sieve of sand that the water left alternately dry; sousing it in the motherly water, bitter, pungent with the salt rinsing, then popped it into the wallets slung over their shoulders. Washerwomen came only to the river because sea water doesn't wash clothes, baskets on head, full of the white week's washing, planting their poles in the sand, stretching their ropes with sure wrist, they fold the big double bed sheets and the spreads covered with white heavy hook-stitch.

The swaddling bands turned three times round the wash lines are gayer than the brides' night gowns with crossed lace. These last if the wind bellied them out seemed stuffed full of decrepit flesh. More amorous the towels with fringes like corn-ears with red mottoes and names interlaced in the corners. The smaller bits are baby blue like the hills of Seravezza after sunset.

All this festooned wash moved a little, as the sea by the beach, as the wings of the gulls, as the mussel fishers, as Cleofe's bosom, as the voice of Don Lorenzo, as the passion of the red faced doctor and Sabina's carnal response, as the suspicion of Don Pietro Galanti and the churning of curses held in by the cowardice of a taciturn husband.

You have sewed me up with black thread, Don Pietro. You have sewed me to your tunic, like a rag button. Black thread don't show on black cloth, no one will see the stiches. But it is fate that I am your servant, even now that I am married. Wait, wait, serve always. Nobody ever waits on me, ever has waited on me.

First I had a job with an old priest in a house with no light, a dark house, now I am servant to a priest who has grown old, even older, and a young priest, and instead of a husband who has the sense to agree with me, I have one who agrees with my boss, if you call it agreeing when he sulks, hides in a corner, lengthens his mug; rolls his eyes as he does when you tell him what you think, Don Pietro.

I was evidently meant to stay bundled up in black thread and mend long black socks worn out heel and toe by priests, sew on black rag buttons, patch soutanes, mend pockets, brush the nap or priest's hats, and their hat cords and bat-wings. And if I go out for a walk and to breathe a breath of clean air with healthy people, first you jump on me, then my husband, and finally Don Lorenzo as if I was married to all of you three.

Life is a black thread bobbin, we live by needle-fulls. But God measures the measure. I am seventy-one, Sabina. I think my life is at its last loop.

You can already see the white on the top of my wooden poll.

Don't be in a hurry, don't curse your servitude. Bear with my old age as I bore with your infancy.

I wish you would think of me as your father, if priests could have children. I brought you up, you may say, with pap and pacifier, and when you were grown I gave you good housing. If you no longer like me, I have been deceived by your benevolence, have you lost the good christian qualities that I taught you?

What do you mean by "your servant even now that I am married." You got married, does that mean that you are to kick over the traces and run wild like a yearling in heat?

If you do, you aren't like your mother of blessed memory. And in saying this Don P.G. got excited. He lost that serenity so habitual to him even in difficult moments.

And Sabina listened to him with irritation as if champing on the bit of a discipline grown insupportable.

The wind turned icy and harsh, the sea roughened and cast off the gulls as if impatient at having tolerated their perching on its rump for so many hours.

The calkers prophesied rain from the heavy flag-like clouds that saddened the heaven. There will be a downpour of big drops before long, pocking the sand waste.

They stretch brown oilskins over the upturned boats, awning'd out a bit further so they can work under them as under a cabin roof. The men looked like journeymen sweeps and lock-smith in orgasm, who on arriving in a country square when it is about to rain find the peasants asking sweeps and tinkers, have they brought the rain and bad luck? Then they look cross and don't have their chimneys done or their kettles fixed, if it rains before the tinkers text are up and the forges and bellows got going.

The calkers push aside ropes and nets, get astride the boats on the part plugged already and calked, and start again tapping the chisels that enlarge the cracks to get out the old tow between plank and plank.

The pitch smoke from the boiling iron cauldrons spreads out low, hanging heavy in the clogging heavy air, hiding the little hunch-back half naked who tends the fire and blows.

I lived with my gran'dad on Monte di Ripa.

My mother worked in the city. My father was dead and I had a brother who had convulsions, who stayed with a woman who looked after him out of charity. That woman was the butcher's wife and helped in the butcher shop and to kill in the slaughter house.

On slaughter days she didn't come home and my brother was alone shut up in the house, and he had convulsions.

They sometimes found him on the floor, as if dead. Sometimes she got drunk and cursed, and beat him.

At carnival he died, and that woman said: blessed paradise!

She had been to the Carnival dance, and came in and stepped on him, then she noticed him. Took the cold body and threw it onto the bed. She took off his checked suit and spread a sheet over my brother whose soul was now safe.

I didn't see him, but I know what he looked like. Once I had seen him twitching on the floor, the door was half open, and the woman who kept him out of charity was at the butcher shop, and I looked through the key-hole and called him.

Then I ran to call her, and when she came back he was stiff.

I didn't see him dead but I can always see him stiff, as he was that day.

My gran'pop, called back to his native earth, called by the house and the town, had come from his travels to stop on in peace.

All his life had been voyage from a dream to a dream, from township to township or to far country.

In his young days the war had taken him as volunteer into its toils. Later, love armed his hand again. But neither love nor war had absorbed him. Now he felt the blood less restive in his veins and less turbid in warming his heart.

Middle high, live glance, biblical beard like my own, thick hair shining like filed iron. Face bright and rosy, thick mulatto's lips like a sucking infant's, he talked of life and death; of Dante, love, early grain crops, manures; half shutting and wide opening his eyes as if fixing an image when he got het up over poetry and things of that sort.

If, on the other hand, he talked of his own past life, of Cleofe, of the mad house, of the way gooks carry on—and he had passed the best part of his life among 'em—his voice grew gentle, he explained things as if he were talking of someone else.

He had the same intonation when he talked of Aladdin lost in the magician's cave among the jewels.

Every now and again he would try to fix a lost detail.

He laughed over his wasted life. It seemed to me odd that he would get into a passion when he talked of the Emperor of Hell with three heads of hideous colour so big he could eat a sinner in each of his three mouths at once. What excited my terrified fancy were the six black wings on the shoulders of so huge an animal, stuck fast to his midriff in ice.

As I had heard that many people sell their souls to the devil to get money in this world, I shook with fear at night, when I thought that my grandpop in some need or other in those far countries might have sold his soul to the devil.

Once he told me that when he was a kid and on the point of drowning he had seen the Madonna.

That made me cry.

We were at the hearth and it was raining. My grandfather had put out the light for economy. The room was lit by the embers. I was on the hearth with the pomeranian bitch. My grandfather on the straw-plaited stool. I hid my teary face in the bitch's yellow coat.

My grandad began to mutter through his teeth, then roared at me: Take down that dog! Put down that dog!

I set the dog on the wooden floor. My gran'dad got up suddenly, opened the door and drove out the dog. That is the way to bring up cowards, instead of men. If I don't die too soon I'll learn ye!

Shut up the stable! Go feed the sheep! He opened the door. The water groaning the gutters splashed on my bare head.

Foscolo was a small sized black dog with rather long thin legs, pointed ears and a tail sticking up.

Our next door neighbor who was older than grandad and as crotchety had taught Foscolo to walk on his hind feet, to bring back stones, to hunt for a hidden handkerchief, to eat raw onions, to drink wine and hold a lighted pipe in his teeth.

Our next and wrathy neighbor came in the evenings to sit at our fire, with a gun slung over his shoulder, with Foscolo as lictor.

The old men got het up and talked of happenings, and I rolled about with the two dogs scraping round on the floor in the dark in the next room.

That sole distraction, I waited for with infantile joy.

Those two dogs were my world.

I was convinced that they knew me by name, I noticed that certain yaps were my name, namely BUCK.

They called me "Buck" by those yelps as I called them by their names.

When Foscolo was tied up by the neighbor's threshing floor, I called him: "Foscolo." He replied with a long howl always the same, so that I knew he was tied. If on the other hand he was loose, he barked pleasantly, jumping around his old master as if asking permissions. Then I knew he was loose and continued to call him. Sometimes he did not ask permission. He came quickly through the vines, made four capers and rushed away.

Even my grandad was fond of Foscolo, because he said our pomeranian bitch had lost her virtue and was no longer any good as a watch dog, since the time she had been carried off with the carts that carry the wine down to the plain of Lucca.

If you give me Foscolo, I'll give you the bitch. Pomeranians are scarce in these parts, and I'll give you a rooster that's a phenomenon, they've promised to bring me from Apulia. It's a cock without claws. It don't scratch. You can leave it loose during seeding time. Eggs that cock makes will be wanted, you can sell 'em high everywhere.

The old neighbor laughed in his face, with his pipe wobbling in his mouth, betting that that clawless rooster was a hoax which my educated grandad wanted to putt over him a poor old contadino.

One evening my grandfather said to our neighbor: It won't be more than a month before Foscolo's stopping here and I bet you won't be able to drag him away even if you chain him and try to.

"Baa' guum, I wanna see thaat." And he kept Foscolo on leash from thence forward.

My yellow bitch began to dance and prance about Foscolo who also got playful. But the blondine raced off, into the shrubs, and came back sidling up and sniffing and moving off with odd movements such as I had observed in unbroken colts.

Catch me if you can, she seemed to say to her fiancé, who looked at her with infantile patience as engaged lovers who play at having secrets and excuse the capriciousness and coaxings as if happy to be more childish than they actually are,

to reduce themselves to greater weakness despite their having double the strength of the weak female

they come to playing blind man's buff

in the hedge like butterflies, like the blondine pomeranian and Foscolo.

My grandfather sent me to call our neighbor and when we got back the fiancés were already married, behind a rose bush.

There you are, old cock, right there in the bed where the violets bloom in April.

But now it is winter and the hummock is green and the rose bush is a bundle of thorns.

But do you think those dry twigs haven't love sap under the ground? Do you think they haven't subterrenian witnesses to their amours, like us watching Foscolo and his blondine?

And do you think this grass-fur hasn't an amorous hook-up under the ground?

You will see, after their pregnancy, their sons will be born, thick on the hills as sand in a river bed. Believe me, old sock, we are the ugliest of the lot. We are all dogs of one breed or another.

Foscolo was now standing quiet, almost asleep with his black muzzle on the yellow pom's neck.

That's it, Buck, that's how your father begot you. And that's how you'll beget yours when you're married.

We are all dogs of one sort or another. It's a shame to talk like that to a kid nine years old, said the peasant.

Tell him with cleaner words, you old buggar, if you can find 'em. How did you come into this world?

And now take away Foscolo and keep him on chain.

Foscolo is no more use now.

Nothing is holy save the field where he has planted his seed, for continuity, or if you like, for immortality.

If we were talking of Buck's seed I would say immortality. Man is made in God's image; and one should burn incense to him.

The old neighbor looked bewildered and scandalized. He looked at me, and moved his shut fist over his mouth, lifted his elbow to ask if grandad was drunk.

I shook my head.

He shut his mouth. Opened his eyes extra wide. Shrugged his shoulders and went off full of suspicion taking Foscolo with him, tied with his leather belt.

Grandpop picked up the bitch and said: Now we must treat her respectfully.

The Apuleian cock was a common and very scrawny rooster with bare scaly legs of egg yellow.

He hadn't even the strut of a cock that serves many hens. He was a bastard little cock who would have become a deballed and crestless capon if my grandfather hadn't bought him from his original peasant owner.

Nothing good about him except his white feathers.

There was a sudden shower the day grandad bought him. The rooster with his legs tied had been chucked on the ground in the shed where we took shelter and had got his wings and belly covered with mud.

When we got home we washed him with water and soap, and so that he shouldn't get dirty again, we put him in a barrel to dry, and in the dark to keep him from crowing.

The downpour had made wash-outs along the banks of the boundary lane and my grandfather noticed that the break was all stones badly piled up, round stones, chunks with no corners such as you find in furrows of fields not before plowed, and that the peasants call field bones.

Grandpop had been going up that border drive for a long time looking at one thing and another, remembering what had been when he was a boy and went to the vineyard to get in the grapes. He got into a row with the old neighbor about a big fig tree which he had seen when new planted and which seemed to him to be too far on the other side of the boundary line.

Now the wash-out showed how the boundary line had been shifted. Grandad began to hum, stroking his beard, when he saw the neighbor coming along a bit thoughtful, saying that the bank was of no importance and that he would see to mending it himself.

Grandpop pretended not to understand and said: Tomorrow that Apuleian rooster will be here.

The neighbor grinned: Hey! by gob, I'll bet you three flasks of old wine. . . .

Late that evening when we were sure the neighbor wouldn't come over that night, grandpop went down to the cellar, took the rooster out of the barrel, put it in a bag and brought it to the house.

He took a pair of pinchers, lit the lamp and said: You remember, Buck, when you were at Querceta, one of the farmer's hens always came into the house? Yes. And when I grabbed it, I said to you: If you speak I'll do you in as I do this hen? Yes. And I cut its head off, and we ate it that night. We put the feathers in a sack and the bones and went and burried 'em a long way from the house? Yes.

All right, Buck, now I tell you: If you speak, I'll pull out your nails, as I propose to pull 'em out of this Apuleian rooster.

I held the cock in the bag, with its feet sticking out; I felt it shake and shudder; and my heart beat and trembled as if I were committing a crime. The cock inside the bag was braced against the table, and the pinchers gripped its claws and used the edge of the table as fulcrum, and you could see the claws come out from the pulp like little teeth from a kid's jaws; and a spurt of black blood came out from the flesh.

Grandad had put on his glasses.

Every now and again he would look into my pallid face. He seemed to enjoy the operation.

When the eight claws were lined up on the table like eight bits of confetti, he heaved a sigh of satisfaction. He put down the tweezers and heated some oil. He anointed the feet of the Apuleian rooster, bound 'em up with bits of rag and took the bird back to the barrel.

The neighbor hadn't been easy and trusting for quite a while and no longer came in of an evening.

He had to be asked several times to come look at the rooster.

He brought Foscolo on lead, and I greeted my friend Foscolo and ran to get the pom for a frolic as usual.

But the dogs seemed almost unacquainted; they hardly said a word to each other, a few mere civilities. I attributed this coldness to Foscolo's iron chain and the neighbor's having tied him to the leg of the table. Foscolo tied up like an assassin felt the humiliation.

The neighbor felt the rooster to see if it was made of real meat, pulled its aenemic wattles, touched its crest with curiosity. There was reddish skin in place of claws which made him think it would grow its claws late.

The rooster walked on the table, slowly, very slowly, gingerly, as if its toes hurt.

Sure! it's a friek!

It's not a friek, its a BREED! Thundered my grandad, and the argument started.

When the old bloke was at the end of his arguments he decided sadly to go get the wine.

It started off as a joke.

Even Foscolo drank a glass of wine. I drank one. Foscolo danced on his hind legs, had a pull at the old man's pipe; then went to sleep under the table because the show was getting damatic.

The old bloke got drunker, then he was afraid of my gran'-dad, thought the scrawny Apuleian cock was a devil. He found the devil's claws in the last glass of wine and was terrified.

He wouldn't believe they were the claws of a mere cock born of a hen.

And my grandfather grinned at him: Look how that rooster is laughin', he's laughin' at *you*. He's got an eye on you. His lookin' at you with only one eye.

The cock was hunched up behind the lamp by the wall.

Every now and again he opened an eye at the sound of grandpop's voice.

Look how he's lookin' at you!

See how red his eye is.

There'll be claws to wake you in hell, you damn thief!

Perhaps you'll turn into a crazy rooster, and the devil will send you to play jokes on old thieves, as this cock's played one on you.

See how red his eye is, going round and round, his eyes are still burnin' with hell fire.

The poor old buffer began to weep.

He made the sign of the cross, then got furious. He reached for his gun and it wasn't there. My grandfather had hidden it first. Then he began to shake, and his teeth rattled as if he had caught a chill.

Then granpop started a devilish conversation with the

rooster. He asked questions in a foreign language, and answered in a different voice.

He paid no attention to the old peasant who begged for mercy, trembling before him and the rooster.

I'm goin' to die. I wanna confess. I don't wanna be damned. Intercede for me Mr. Rooster.

And he clasped his hands before the cock, and finally got down on his knees on the floor.

Then granpop put a chair near him and put the rooster on it and then said: I am the Holy Ghost. Confess! Confess!

My grandad was right. The fig tree was too far from the boundary.

For fifty years our neighbor had taken the stones which came up with digging and plowing, and carried them to the boundary, and thus his land had spread over a yard and a half all along the edge. His property had been cleared, fondled from one end to the other.

In his vineyard the wine was now better because the old buzzard has shaken up the earth, taken out stones, taken out the bad vines, rooted up strawberry grapes and planted columbine and aleatico grapes.

Now the christian labourer was old and about to die. He was leaving a perfect vineyard to his family and was receiving from God the reward of his labours, the sight of the Apuleian holy ghost to whom he could confess his sins before getting ready to pass on . . . a divine favour.

That's what my grandpop told him, and took him home late when the jag began to wear off.

On the way back we stopped near the fig tree. Grandpop paced off the distance to the boundary. I looked at the moon low over the sea. I saw the ligurian hills and the roofs of the towns in the plain.

Two gun shots, one right after the other.

And the rattle of shot in the frosty grass between my bare feet, like the points of poison thorn, made me jump gasping: The old boy has shot himself!

No! he wanted to shoot us.

And grandad started down the boundary lane, talking of the frost that was bad for the vine shoots.

We passed the rest of that winter alone, grandad and I in the evenings with the light out.

I on the hearth stone, and grandpop on the straw stool, by the fire, the brand was of luminous olive wood and gave a lot of cinders and very little flame.

Long boring evenings ending with yawns so steady as to make young Buck weep, despite his being all ears and alert to hear the true fairy tales of his grandpop, illustrated by examples, coloured with pictures of clear poetry and sombre drama; telling how the lunatics with whom he had lived 24 years fell in love with the new moon. They prepared curious wreaths of flowers for her, without leaves, five or seven kinds with the same number of unspotted petals, a real certosian and geometric field, studied and worked out lovingly with a smile on their lips, their eyes bright and absorbed.

And there are other nice lunatics so gentle they can call the birds with names you have never heard. Until they see birds in the sky, fabulous, all made of air, invisible and transparent. Others talked with the wind and with field flowers. Or they praised God from year's end to year's end, standing still in a corner with their eyes turned up to heaven and their arms folded.

Others have no use for talk, tongue doesn't work, they would stand mute for ages, guarding what secrets?

But if the lunatics had cut open their bellies for love . . . Or others, in sleep, stabbed with crazy jealousy, had strangled those whom they ought to have loved all their lives, and now wept because they were dead, and reappeared to them in sleep. . . . They saw them upright, steady, still in the garden cross-walk, waiting till they could get out of that prison to be reunited and go on to heaven knows where. . . .

Generous, impatient outbursts of that blond young fellow, all eyes and sinews of steel, jammed into a strait jacket near my grandfather's bed in the first days: Near the big window . . .

He SAW her, he lept up to go to her, and she always turned off toward the shrubbery and didn't see him. And didn't see his chained love, and he was tied up by his rival who wanted to steal her from him . . .

But who couldn't because now he had written to the queen, and she will come with coach and footmen and maid servants to free him.

But in the meanwhile *she* has turned off by the myrtles and don't know this. Let the queen come and she will fix it O.K.

It grows dark and *she* is still there by the standing still.

Perhaps she is chained and don't hear, and don't see her lover behind the barred window, in pain, crying out, and making signs. But he can't call her by name because her name is made up of letters that aren't in the alphabet any longer.

And the women that so terrified me in my grandfather's stories, women turned into mooing buffaloes in bestial conjunctions in the marshes of the maremma. I can still see them going on all fours prodded on by pock-marked guardians in white overalls.

And the others that tear off their clothes without knowing why, and have lost all shame and talk excitedly with the men without suspicion of sex, and at night roll up in the moonlight like hedgehogs in underbrush.

Violent men that had killed many kings of the earth so that mankind might be sated with goods, who support your chains with pride, and shake every now and again and tug at the straps that bind you. To run again to your place of combat in the world, shoving it along with mighty heaves so that it will revolve more quickly. Beautiful and terrible your bloody fury! How many times have you slept with me on my cot, with the few coverlets in those long winter nights.

Don't kill me. I am not a king's son.

And I would wake up and think of the sons of kings born with such cruel destinies. One does not know why God puts so heavy a burden on their shoulders.

And those women huddled weeping on the ground from morning till evening.

Undone, because they have forgotten, lost something they can not find again.

And they bend over, opening their eyes wide and full of tears. These lanterns lit on a rainy night, to hunt in the corners, in the cracks of the pavement, in the chinks of the wall.

They have lost something. What have they lost? They wander about sobbing like marmosets, souls in purgatory paying their sins, seventy years for each lie.

And look at the doctors with eyes half shut, leering at the other women of whom they are jealous. They walk along scraping the walls, with little short steps so as not to be seen and recognized; and all day and every day with their hands tied, because if the doctor unties them, they will begin to scratch their mons veneris till the blood comes, as if they had a herd of lice there at pasture.

This was the son of a luchese emigrant.

He had lost his reason in an american forest, and lost his way home. He made friends with the apes in the forest, eating nuts and wild fruit. He slept in the trees for fear of snakes, he became a thin ape with long nails and a hairy face. But carnivorous teeth wanted meat. Therefore in bad weather he ate the carcasses killed and left by the other wild animals.

He was found by relatives, peasants near the forest. Recognized, captured, like a wild animal he tried to bite them, refused food, let out guttural howls like an ape and roared like a lion.

Thus he was brought back to his native country, and my grandfather knew him in the days of his adventure.

I followed him step by step on his return voyage. He followed, he began to call his father, then he remembered his smallest sister.

He learned to smile. When the doctor pricked him with a needle he felt it. And man is man on condition that he feels pain always in two ways; that he feels grief for a distant family, and pricks on live cured flesh.

His cure was rapid. He got well before my grandad, so that he became his nurse and consoler.

My grandfather despaired of getting well, getting over the

flow of madness that every now and again centupled his strength and drove him to devastation.

After the cure of the luchese emigrant, he understood that he too would get well.

You must want to get well said the luchese with kind words, when my grandfather lost hope.

Unless they want to, nobody will ever get well.

Thus he had to want to get well, use his will to get well. And my grandfather began to want nothing except to get well.

Not that the luchese emigrant was dirty, quite the contrary, but this was because it was more beautiful to be clean than dirty; not because dirtiness makes men ill. On that point no one could shake him. He didn't believe in contagion and laughed at the doctors' meticulous hygiene.

Eleven million microbes can get onto the sticky side of a postage stamp.

Alive? interrupted the luchese emigrant, looking clever.

Alive enough to bump you off in a very few hours. But can eleven million living creatures that I can stick onto the end of my thumb be that powerful and invisible all at once?

That was something the luchese couldn't understand. Sometime he thought the medicoes had heard this hocus-pocus from the lunatics.

When peculiarities mentioned in the story were shared by one of our acquaintance, my grandfather would say: A drop or two more or less will make the jug slop over; another drop and the jug will slop over.

That chap would be a nuisance or dangerous. And his relatives or someone would put him on a closed wagon and cart him off to the gook house up there past Monte Quiesa, and down the Sercio valley and then up that little hill, and shut him there in the sanctuary, where he'd have a much better time.

No one is totally sane.

No one is totally crazy, it's a matter of balance, measured in the interests of the half crazy who decide about their half sane fellow men.

How often have I heard: He's a good chap, but just a bit enthusiastic.

Or: he goes off at full moon.

That's his weak point, don't try that on him.

He's got a bit of smoke in his top story, gets all het up over nothing.

He lies like a trooper, always digging up something.

Watch 'em when they get drunk, give 'em an extra drop and they get so kindly, kindly, so kindly.

Laugh like hell and roar like the devil.

Can't stand up, and blame it on the earth's goin' round.

Another one will grab a knife and think everyone's against him.

Have you ever seen drunks start pissing and dumping like beasts in front of everyone else?

It's a matter of degree.

The rich can go further than poor folks.

In every rich family there are at least two, if there are four in the family, who would get shut up in the sanctuary of Frigonaria but their parents, mostly doctors with stinking sores, put up with 'em and excuse 'em, and say: Little horsey will stop when he's run himself tired.

In the mean time rich folk's crazy children go on squandering what their parents have welched out of poor lunatics.

There is a law of compensation even in this:

"See my house."

And he came back: Pleasant to sleep in April.

April's way comes down barrel a day.

Grumpy, Don Lorenzo and Cleofe. The red faced doctor, Sabina, Don Pietro Galanti in the wagon, in the spring, coming back to the village.

Those are the names of the lunatics. Grumpy. And now Don Lorenzo. Cleofe's fever came back, the pain, the sleeplessness, the enervating sweats. She went back to bed for a week, seriously ill.

Then she got better.

And thus it went on till October, when the streets of Seravezza rustle with leaves and thistles, blown down from the mountain with the first frisky wind.

Again appears Grumpy with his head bundled up, with his ear glued to key-holes, listening for the doctor's voice and Sabina's, who no longer slept in his bed:

She had had a girl child that looked like the red-faced doctor, with red hair and a freckly face.

If he got ill there was that doc, Jack of Clubs at the door: won't die of that, takes more than that to kill 'em.

Or he ordered a medicine which Grumpy didn't take because it might have poison in it.

The veins swelled on his neck, he got red as a peperone.

There was no doubt of it, the red head persecuted him. Jack of Clubs came and said they should bleed him.

Grumpy was scared and objected. He knew that his time had come. Jack of Clubs wanted to kill him and get Sabina, who was now his whore and had had a child by him, which Grumpy couldn't bear to touch.

He felt aversion for blood not his own. He couldn't stand that reddish fuzz and the scabs on the top of its head.

Even Don Pietro Galanti couldn't get a word out of him.

Nothing for it but to recommend him to God.

Jack of Clubs said he ought to go amuse himself for a month in a city to get rid of his hypochondria, and Grumpy knew it was just to get him out of the house.

The Doc said: Even Lucca. And Grumpy knew the gook house was in Lucca, where his poor brother was.

But you got to get over this mania, said the Doc. And Grumpy cowered down under the bed clothes, waiting to be copped.

He heard 'em saying the one lunger was no worse and that she was getting better, and Grumpy knew that he was the one who was going to die, that Jack of Clubs needed to keep Cleofe alive in order to be able to drop in at any time.

With Cleofe as excuse he could come in and enjoy Sabina and see his maggoty brat.

And he, Grumpy, couldn't say anything, for fear of those shiny scalpels that the doc had in his leather case.

One of those little knives could make a little hole in his skull and the blood would come out a drop at a time, and even those few drops were a sea without port or harbour.

He thought he might kill Cleofe.

She was so full of t.b. she would die sometime sooner or later. But he wouldn't have had the courage to die.

He thought of arguing it out with the abbé, might find some complicated way to convince him; the abbé could do it, always in Cleofe's bed-room.

But when he opened his mouth to start explaining to the abbé, with the long argument that he had been chewing over for days, and masticating inside his groggy head-piece, Don Pietro Galanti appeared at the door.

Grumpy felt his tongue swell up between his teeth, and he couldn't get his mouth shut again.

He locked himself in his room.

He remembered his mother, dead without the sacraments and with one eye open.

Believe in God's punishment!

He hung himself with the cord they used to hang out the maggoty brat's dirty diapers.

"I never wanted to ask how Cleofe died."

She must have faded out bit by bit with solemn humility: Without useless sighs.

Without wasting a breath, must have closed her snuff-coloured eyes.

Don Pietro Galanti probably said to the red-faced doctor: It's a pleasure when they die that way, just little by little.

At least there is time for the sacraments; neither too soon nor too late. And get to heaven before other sins can get onto their soul. . . .

I heard she was dead, years later, when they thought I was cured.

The nuns brought me your mother in the Campana Institute uniform. I knew like a shot, and made a sign that they shouldn't say anything; for the pity I felt seeing the child in those ridiculous clothes.

BEFORE DEATH

AHMED ALI

I shall arise and go now. My life has been one long series of pain, and in the eyes of the world my presence rankled like a thorn. When the thorn is removed the consciousness of pain would of itself disappear. My life was a blot on the face of Beauty; and when I am gone its lovers will rejoice. They that loved flowers hated me, for I was a parasite living on their favorite flower. Everyone desired the object, but my presence repulsed them. That which is ugly has no right to live. But I had no hold over Life and Death. I too loved Beauty; and I too hated Ugliness. But I could neither kill my love nor deny the others the right to love. Life was my beloved and I its unhappy lover. Wherefore should I have come in the way of others? But now I feel that I was so ugly that I repulsed even Beauty. My life was a mirage, so beautiful a dream that on waking, it proved unreal. I had taken refuge from ugliness in the lap of a wilderness every extremity of which is frightening and every particle of sand heart-rending and dull. The events of the past surge back into my brain. The ache of my heart has come to whisper again. . . .

In the courtyard of my house stood a dried-up tree; a victim of an unknown disease. Perhaps, the white ants had set

132

at its roots and the heat of the sun had scorched and blackened its bark. Now all that was left were a trunk and two
branches that stood poised like a trident against the sky.
When in the evening I raised my eyes and looked upon it, I
was reminded of the Hunter of Death about to strike the
Heavens. And often at night I felt that I was that hunter
poised in the darkness to hit the sky with the sun. The net-
work of the stars would break and the Milky Way would
lose itself into the depths of Eternity. But the tree would
stand like an eternal fool with meaningless hands stretched
loosely towards the sky gazing so that I would be livid with
rage at its utter stupidity and wished only to fell it with an
axe to the ground. In the unending vastness of the night the
two branches of the tree looked like the pincers of an ant
painfully piercing the flesh.

It so happened that a famine-stricken woman lay down beneath it. Perhaps there was an eternal bond between them,
and because they were both immature and stunted imbeciles
they had recognised and embraced each other. Passing by the
tree in the morning what should I find but a shriveled woman,
lying dead with arms entwined round the tree and a child
clung to her sucking the lifeless breasts. He would suck and
pull at them and failing to find any milk would let them go
and, enraged, howl and rub his feet on the ground. The eyes
of the woman had sunk into their sockets but on her lips was
a frozen smile. She was naked, and her bony, black legs were
outstretched like the branches of the tree. Her head was resting against the trunk and her legs seemed but the shadow of
the prongs of a trident. The expression on her frightening
face filled me with dread. But two things worried me: the
meaning of the smile on the woman's lips, and the efforts of
the child in sucking the breasts. Was Death laughing at Life?
Was Life seeking life from Death?

This may have been so. For Death is present in Life's do-
main, though in the valley of Death there is no Life. And I
shall yearn for the emotions which in Life were the enemies
of the heart and waylaid awareness and faith. Neither will
there be these breezes which enliven dead souls nor the be-

witching ways of the beautiful ones. There will not be the crows that deprive you of every moment of peace, nor these vultures that thrive on the living. As time draws near for me the love for living increases manifold. But then everything leaves me weary. My heart turns away with disgust from Life's playthings, and everything seems futile and vain. All that my heart desires is that the quicker I find release from this useless sorrow and meaningless strife which stops at failure and pain, the sooner I shall win my freedom from the forces of circumstance. After wasting the whole of life came the understanding that the desire for faith is avarice and the search for truth a deceptive lie. Whyfore seek what resides in your heart? Wherefore wander from forest to forest and desert to desert? We are either unable to hear the voice of conscience, and if we do, we wander in the hope of forgetting it. But either way we find no rest.

A clergyman used to visit me. Tall in height, of large hands and feet, on his oval face his long and acquiline nose and goatlike, pointed beard created the impression of a cactus on a desert rock. He usually wore a *dhoti* through which could be seen ill-proportioned legs like two bamboo sticks. He used to wobble with an undignified gait making one feel that he must fall at the next step. But his spadelike feet supported his falling structure. To sit on a chair meant the lighting of a much-used pipe followed by quick, hard pulls and a trickling of saliva onto his beard. In the heat of an argument he would lose himself in a spate of Christian eloquence and with much sobbing and sighs begin to sing hymns; and his voice would make the noise of a bellows and the heaving of his breath could be heard like hissing flames.

He often held forth on religious matters. Though much impressed by Hindu religion he could not understand the democratic principles of Islam. He was always suspicious of there being a secret motive behind the simple teachings of Mohammad. The intricacies of transmigration seemed to him much simpler in comparison to the Muslim explanation of Life-after-Death. The complexities of the Holy Ghost presented no difficulties as opposed to the Muslim belief that

God communicated with His Prophet through the angel Gabriel. His greatest complaint was that when economics and politics were a part and parcel of its theology, how then could Islam be a revealed religion? In his opinion no religion could be called a religion unless it incorporated mysteries. That is why he could not differentiate between Islam and Communism. The only difference that he was ready to acknowledge was that if Islam was the dictatorship of Allah, Communism was the dictatorship of Stalin; and both he disliked intensely.

One evening when I had peace of mind, who should intrude but the clergyman. During conversation we touched upon the subject of Trinity. With childish playfulness I said, "You people have turned an essentially human doctrine into a spiritual and difficult problem."

"I don't follow you," the clergyman said.

"According to you," I replied, "The Trinity consists of the Father, the Son and the Holy Ghost."

"What else could it be?" he interrupted.

"It could be and couldn't be."

"Then, do you think there is some meaning other than that meaning?"

"I dare not insinuate that you are a liar. But you know that all religions give a spiritual color to human wisdom and experience. The way in which Abraham came to acknowledge the existence of God shows the progress of the human mind. And as life became involved, religion also became more complex. So that the authority of the ruling and priestly classes may not be questioned one finds that they started sanctifying their laws and rulings. It is as a result of this that the Christians evolved the doctrine of the Trinity. What you call the Father, the Son, and the Holy Ghost are, in fact, God, Man, and Conscience. The Son of God is man and Satan his tempter. . . ."

At this stage of the argument the clergyman stood up livid with rage and started shouting hysterically. He began to foam at the mouth and the saliva trickled onto his beard and clothes. His *dhoti* came undone and his bamboo-thin legs looked like the shadow of the tree in the courtyard. He then stretched out his hands as if he was going to strangle me. His long and bony fingers looked like dry intertwined branches of a tree. While thus anxious I suddenly heard the air raid sirens pierce the night and the roar of hundreds of multiengined aircraft in the distance. The lights were switched off at the mains. As the lights went out I could hear the bursting of bombs around us. I found the clergyman lying behind the chairs stretched out on the floor as if clasping the earth, and looked like a frog floating on the surface of the water. Instinctively I took shelter in the corner of the room and was mortified. At this moment I realized that one is punished for his sins even while alive. . . .

For a long time after this incident we did not meet. One day I had walked longer than usual. It was that time of evening when Death overpowers Life and the darkness of night begins strangling the light of day. In the distance stood a range of hills and a winding road came down to meet the plains. Silence had descended upon all things and even the crows were silent. It had rained during the day and beyond the hills, across the dark clouds, a streak of yellow ochre was dimly visible. Here and there water stood in pools and puddles; and the reflections of the hills, the sky, and the clouds created a mystic atmosphere. The soulful breeze stirred the blood in my veins, and I was lost in a faraway world of colorless and somber dreams. The ache of my heart was in banishment like Ram* and Lakshman, and the thought of Sita did not ruffle my calm. At that moment I had overcome all sorrows of the world, the fear of famine and war. I had merged into nature and having become one with her had permeated the universe as its master and lord. Lost in thought I walked like the breeze caressing the face of the beloved, with hands folded at the back, when I heard a plaintive voice full of humility, "What did you say, O Lord?"

---

* Hero of the *Ramayana*, who was banished from his kingdom for a long period. Lakshman, his brother, and Sita, his wife, volunteered to go with him where Sita was kidnapped by Ravan who caused them great pain.

Possibly the voice had sounded in my ears before, but I was so lost in reverie that I could not have heard it. When I gradually became conscious of the voice my hair stood on end. I did not hear the tread of feet, but the voice sounded nearer and louder every minute. I tried to turn round to look, but fear held me back. Soon I felt somebody saying close by, "What did you say, O Lord?" I looked to see the clergyman on a bicycle. Probably he too was lost in thought and had not noticed me either.

"Is all well with you?" I asked. "Who were you talking to?" He got down from the bicycle, but his face was flushed with the creepy yellow of the lizard's skin. For a few moments he stood still as though his soul was being rent. My fear increased, and much perturbed I said, "For God's sake say something. Are you ill?"

With great effort he wetted his upper lip with his tongue and said in a trance, "When I pedal my feet to a particular position then I feel that God wishes to speak to me; but before I can hear, the position of my feet on the pedals has changed and I hear nothing."

On hearing his voice I heaved a sigh of relief. I was at first wonder-struck at what he said; then I felt like laughing and said, "Why don't you stop pedaling so that you could hear the voice of God?"

"That is the wonder of it all," he said. "The voice only comes when the wheel has completed one rotation; and if I stop pedaling the voice is heard no more, and then is audible only when my feet are in a particular position. But before God can complete His message my feet have moved."

Having said this he turned towards the heavens, "O Holy Ghost, come and possess me so that all the mysteries may be revealed to me. For I am dying in my death and the deaths of those after me, for Thou art the Father and I am Thy son. . . ."

I wished to ask, "Who then, is the Holy Ghost?" But the expression on the clergyman's face was so weird that I could not speak. On it had spread the yellow tint of the dark clouds, the eyes had receded into their sockets, and on the dry beard the tears were dropping as rain drops on a tiled roof. The bicycle was leaning against his body and his hands were joined in prayer. At that moment they seemed not the hands of a living being, but the hands of Death. But as soon as he finished the prayer he rode away and was soon lost in the darkness of the night. . . .

On reaching home I sat down in a chair wondering and worried to the extent of becoming oblivious of the light in the room. I was not even conscious of the fact that I was in my own house. Nothing disturbed my thoughts. Only now and then lightning flashed in the distance as though in another world; and with the soughing of the breeze the silence became more grave. I know not how long I sat in desolation with my thoughts. The sudden ringing of the telephone brought me back to reality. But when I put the receiver to my ear I was still lost in the world of imagination. The voice asking for me at the other end was so strange and otherworldly that it sent a sensation of fear down my back. It had the ring of an echo which ebbed and flowed like the waves and reached the secret depths of my soul. When I asked who it was, the answer was one which made me gasp for breath. Thus I thought there was surely some mistake, and I asked in a frightened voice, "Who? Who is speaking?"

From that end the same ringing voice came back into my ears, "I am God. This is God speaking."

If cut at that moment I would not have shed a drop of blood. I started shivering like one in the grips of fever. The receiver dropped and I was startled by the noise of its falling. Was I dreaming? But in the heart of my heart I said to myself, "Could it be possible that God Almighty, the Creator of the Universe, should talk to me, an insignificant and sinful creature. Surely I was laboring under a delusion. With a stout heart I replaced the receiver to my ear and said with effort, "I am extremely sorry that I did not follow. Will you kindly repeat your name again. . . ."

For a long time I waited for an answer, but heard nothing. All that was audible was silence, deeper than the night and darker than the clouds. With fright I sat down in a chair and closed my eyes.

When I recovered I sent for the carriage. As I was coming out of the room a flash of lightning revealed the dried-up tree standing like a nightmare with outstretched arms in the darkness of the night. On one of the branches sat an owl in silence. As I stepped into the carriage the shrill hooting of the owl pierced the night, but the horses moved on.

The carriage was driven with speed. It was now passing over the narrow and cobbled road of a town, and the grating noise of the wheels sounded like the falling of water on the rocks. A jolt of the carriage made me sit up and look through the window. We were passing by an expensive shop. Its large glass windows were flooded with light. I had not yet been able to take in the marvel I beheld when my eyes were fixed in a stare on a window. A colossal black and shiny crow with lanky legs as long as those of a man was cawing and cawing and selling bones; and to attract the attention of passers-by was throwing them up and about with his ugly beak creating the impression of a puppet dance. I looked at this ungainly spectacle with such fascination that I felt I too had become a bone. Meanwhile the crow saw me and stretched its beak toward me. Taking me to be a bone, it was about to pick me up when the carriage moved forward and stopped at the second window.

Here could be seen a vulture directing a dance of hands, feet, bones and skulls of human beings. During their movement in the air these parts of the human anatomy looked as if they were the complete body of a man moving like a mechanical skeleton, but when the movement came to an end and the skeleton fell to the ground, each limb was separated. Then one by one hands, feet and skulls vanished; and the vulture, with wings outspread, sat resting on its tail, like an advertisement in a taxidermist's shop. When it cast its eyes upon me they began to glow and a smile appeared on its face. It sharpened its beak and stretched its ugly neck toward me. The pin feathers on its neck stood up like thorns and as it drew near, the blood in my veins congealed with fright; and the expression of joy on its face turned to one of hatred. I crouched in a corner of the carriage. The vulture's neck was now in the window. It stared at my frightened face and laughed madly. I became hysterical with dread, but the carriage again moved forward at the moment with a jolt. My ears were humming and perspiration flowed down my body. Darkness reigned all around. The coachman whipped the horses to a gallop.

As my breath came back to me I shouted, "Where are you taking me? Turn back home."

"Address me properly! Don't you know who you are talking to?"

It was not the voice of my coachman. But I thought that he had had too much to drink, and I said angrily, "Don't natter! Come to your senses!"

The carriage stopped suddenly and the coachman turned round and looked at me. On seeing him I lost my senses, for it was not my coachman but a dreadful-looking stranger. In one hand he held the reins, and in the other a whip at whose end was tied an ear of wheat* and it looked like a snake. On his dark face his black beard looked like a smudge on the nocturnal sky. From his unearthly inhuman face it seemed that he knew all the secrets of Time and Space, and neither could sorrow come near him nor joy divert him from his purpose. He fixed me with a stare. One of his eyes had such magnetism that I perforce looked on with mesmerical fascination and became oblivious of everything. In the dirty white of the eye were concentric circles of brown as if layers of brown colored glass had been imposed and super-imposed on each other and blended into the shape of the retina. The center was a pupil of black stone. Then suddenly the man's face dissolved into that of a woman who had a thousand wrinkles and a toothless mouth. But the eye did not even blink and held me imprisoned in the stare. Then the colors of the eye began to fade as when an object clearly seen at a distance is brought

* The Muslim version of the Fall gives wheat as the "forbidden fruit," and not the apple.

nearer to the eye and is blurred; and in its place appeared the secret darkness of a mountain cave. The eye closed and disappeared, but the blackness remained. My heart thumped hard and fear gripped me in its claws. My throat was parched and I could not stir even to shut my eyes. But then fear itself came to my rescue. In me all the forces of life were awakened and I shook my will back to life. The eye, the hag and the darkness vanished into the night; but the images of the eye were efflorescing on the surface of my consciousness. As I was about to drown in a sea of eyes, I mustered courage and jumped out. There were neither the carriage, the horses nor the coachman. I stood alone before a wall.

The wall was of a fort on a hill, and I was on my way to my destination. Walking on the parapet I reached a point from where rose a higher wall onto which I climbed, thus leaving the straight path. A few steps ahead of me the wall was broken and I could not walk further. On that little bit of the wall I stood marooned, unbefriended and alone. Neither could I move on nor retrace my steps. Despair, solitude and helplessness encircled me. Love in the universe, rejoicings in the world, but here was neither Adam nor any of his breed, nor singing birds nor any sign of life or being. Only the blames of the earth and the despair of the deserts were lamenting for me. I then decided that in descending alone lay salvation. The ascent was easy, the descent proved difficult. While clutching the wall to come down, the realization of height and the mortal fear of the fall into depth made the light in my eyes fail. Thousands of feet below in the heart of the valley threaded a veinlike stream, but no sound of its waters reached my ears. A fog enveloped the mountains and a mist lay heavy over the valley; and the rocks and trees seemed but their shadows. My head swirled; the earth was dust; and it seemed as if the wall would escape from my hands.

My not falling was a miracle. And in the winking of an eye all sense of fear was lost. I walked the parapet as I would a broad road. In the foreground could be seen the arch of my destination. There was the temple in search of which I had wandered from forest to desert, from land to land. The light brown of its walls was clearly visible; and the line where the arch had been worked in and the patch where the lime had fallen stood out in relief. I quickened my pace. The wall met a broad roof. I looked not back for the past was left behind me.

The roof was aged, and its color had blackened with sun, rain, and time. Here and there a lighter color showed. There was a low mound stretched around, and I walked fearlessly to the other end. But the adjoining structures had fallen long ago and there was no way forward. Sadness overcame me. There was no hope of reaching the desired destination.

To jump was the only alternative. With outstretched arms I plunged into space. There was a time when I could fly, but the limbs had now become weary and dragged so that I had lost the power of flight. With difficulty I glided heavily past the lower battlements of the fort and came to civilization. The first thing that I saw were the ruins of homes on the fringe of the city. Some of the roofs had fallen and the debris had blocked the stairways; and some appeared heaps of earth and stone. I entered the city through the Royal Gate. The roads and boulevards were clean, but a ghostly silence shadowed everything. I walked past the Grand Mosque. I was certain that there would be life here; but everything was quiet. It seemed that the place was deserted and inhabited only by the *jins.* Those lanes and streets and bazars through which my steps had resounded a thousand times now seemed dead with no sign of men or beasts or human habitation. Walking through the garden I came to the Private Baths and desirous of bathing passed through the low, dark chambers and came to the tank. When I had taken off my clothes and come to its edge I found there was not a drop of water. The floor lay clean and the four walls reached out to the skies. I was so tired that I sat down in a corner. I felt that I was one with the walls, the mausoleums and the ruins; and Time and Space fell away from my mind and were lost. I was at the same time eternal and unreal. What was and what was not were both beyond my consciousness and within its orbit. While I sat lost in this state a gust of wind brought human voices to my ears. They came from above. "I say, O friend, look at that bird. It seems to be a skylark."

"You seem to be right," the other said. "There it flies. Do you see? How it soars into the heavens and floating, looks upon the earth and sings and sings like fireworks going off into the sky."

Along with this came the sound of a bird singing, but very faintly, as if from a great distance. "Its nest must be in that *babool* tree. We shall soon know when it comes down."

"Well, friend, let's plan to catch it. For it's difficult nowadays to lay hands on a skylark."

"Then let's go and look for the nest. What say you, Wrestler?"

"As you wish. I am ready. . . ."

The voices died out. The men walked away. No sooner had they gone than a tired voice came from the same direction, "Brothers, dust to dust . . ." This was followed by the sound of footsteps and falling earth.

For a long time I sat quietly with my head against the wall. I knew not if I was dead or alive. In this state of oblivion the voices sounded once again. These voices were new and strange and were coming from beyond the walls of the adjoining rooms. The first voice was playful and sharp. "Your grace, do you know that a new courtesan has arrived today?"

"What! Where?" exclaimed a drunken and sleepy voice. "Then we must see her."

"She is towards your feet, your grace. The inebriety has not yet left her. But it won't be for long. Rajjan Khan, are you still asleep?"

"No your lordship," said the third. "I am waiting for Rajan Bai."

"So, she is called Rajan Bai, is she?"

"Then there are two Rajans now, aren't there?"

"Well said Nawab Sahib. Ha, ha, ha!"

"What have you to say then, Rajjan Khan?"

"Your grace has only to command. A song, a tune on the flute, or the sound of the drum . . ."

"Hey, you haven't told us who she really is?"

"How shall I answer your grace? She has left the profession and become very chaste. She used to recite the poems of Hafiz of Shiraz, and pray all day. But, ah, your grace, she had 'oomph' in her. And, of course, in singing she had no equal."

"Then she is the one for our Mir Sahib. If we arrange a match between her and him, what say you, how will it be?"

"Ha, ha, ha! Well said, your grace. None else but you could have said it," answered the sharp and playful voice; and the laughter resounded like a crescendo.

"Look here, Nawab Sahib, I have told you a hundred times that there is an extent to your joking. I may be poor, but I am a cultured person. I loved my wife," said the sad voice of an unhappy lover.

"O forget it. What's Love to do with Beauty? One is the voice of sex, the other is a proportion of joints and limbs. . . ."

"Then what's the difference between the two, O sir?" said a somber voice.

"One is the voice of the heart; the other is harmony and grace."

"Hey, that's exactly what I said. Love is Beauty's veil. . . ."

"Wrong!" said the same voice again. "Not a veil, but a reflection. Love is Beauty, and Beauty is Truth."

"You have started cooking philosophy. If, on the other hand, you had cooked your pulses, the presentation of your case would have been more solid," said the Nawab Sahib, and a peal of laughter rang forth.

Before the laughter could die down the beautiful voice of a woman could be heard singing:

> *"I have seen the image of my love*
> *Within the sparkling glass:*
> *O you who do not know the joy*
> *Of eternal wine alas!"* *

From all sides voices of "well done, well done, encore, encore" rose high. Then the Nawab asked, "Pray, who may this be?"

* This and the following verses are from the Persian of Hafiz.

"Why, Rajan Khan, this seems to be of your doing."

"Huzoor, this is she. Did I not say?"

"Brother, well done. Allah be praised. May she live long. How beautifully she rendered each word. When such is the sweetness of her throat, what a marvel of beauty must she be?"

"Huzoor, the chin a star, the forehead a veritable moon. To see is to behold."

"Then she must be seen. . . . Damn it, have you gone to sleep again?"

"Can that be possible, your grace? I have been lost in her charm. Look, behold, with what abandon she is rising."

"Hey, I see nothing."

"She is towards your feet, your grace. Let her arise."

In the meantime came the voice of a broken heart:

> *Be not the troublemaker with your curls*
> *Spread out upon your shoulder:*
> *My sad heart cannot bear the pain of grief*
> *Alas, not any longer.*

"Is all well? This seems to be Manjnoon awakened. It is he, is it not?"

"Correctly said, your grace. This is all Rajjan Bai's doing. Listen, for she is about to sing again."

> *"Come out of the palace of my heart*
> *Without a fear of man, unveiled;*
> *For there is none else resident there*
> *Besides your love—all else has paled."*

Majnoon heaved a sigh. The Nawab said: "Grace be to God"; and voice of "well done, well done" rent the air.

"Now I can't wait any longer."

"I await your lordship's command," said Rajan Khan.

"But I have no money. Do you hear or are you lost?"

"In your grace's presence can I be guilty of such misdemeanor? As for the money, what is the Sethji for? It's there for the asking. May your star remain in ascendency. There you are. See, there comes Sethji himself, and in what style!

With the ledger under his arm, his hand massaging his paunch, he is on the way to the shop."

"What are you doing? For goodness sake, stop him!"

"Did you say something to me?" said Sethji suddenly stopping.

"Are you dumb?" whispered the Nawab. "Ask him for ten thousand."

But Sethji of himself replied, "Look, Nawab Sahib, first pay off your debts. To date the interest itself amounts to over one and a half lakh. If the account is not settled I shall be obliged to go to the law."

"Don't do that, for goodness sake! Every bit of your money will be returned. But right now we need money very badly. . . ."

While this conversation was going on there was noise and commotion all around. Loud voices were heard:

"I have been killed," one shouted.

And another, "She is a witch; who allowed the bitch to come here?"

A woman cried hysterically, "Let me also see the whore. It was she who ruined my husband. . . ."

A crowd seemed to have collected and nothing but noise could be heard. Then the hoofs of galloping horses sounded on the road; and a voice of authority shouted, "Thrash the swine! What you gaping at, Mangal Khan! Charge with your horse, Badal Singh."

The noise of wailing and lamentation rent the air; and the sound of falling bodies was heard. Then the voice of authority shouted again, "If the bastards don't disperse shoot them down. Company, fire!" Cannons thundered; then all of a sudden quiet prevailed as if nobody was there. Silence became frightening and I walked toward my house.

Darkness had descended upon the earth. Night reigned supreme. But here and there flames were shooting up into the air, and from over the horizon came the noise of returning aircraft. When I reached my locality I found that area had been heavily bombed. Not a building stood intact. My heart missed a beat.

Pressing my sorrow to my breast, worried and anxious, I started climbing onto the rubble and debris of destruction. As far as the eye could scan one saw nothing but ruins and remains. The buildings and factories nearabout were still burning; and red, green, blue and other colorful flames were lighting up the earth and the sky. All of a sudden my eyes fell on the tree in my courtyard. There it stood as it always had. It did not seem a tree but the God of Destruction with arms upraised in a dance of Death. The fire of hate leapt up in my heart, but between myself and it stood a mountain of flames; and I could not reach the tree. I stood where I was with head held high in pride as though I was the monarch of the earth and the sky. And the wind and the flames wove a net of music all around me. . . .

CIPANGO'S HINDER DOOR

EDWARD DAHLBERG

For My Wife R'lene

I

I chant energy and chance to youth,
And to the old I bring
The mulled wine of ancient annals.
Strife is a demigod that parents our acts,
Eats the land,
And has created a race of dog-necked people
With bitter fangs of reason.

O people take the purgative buckthorn
And the laurel for parturition.
Sons of little-born dust,
Your birth is in the bones of gods and fathers
Whose annals you know not;
Let history be your hymn of penance,
Farm your parents and the races in the ground,
Not for pelf but for remembrance,
And make ready for the festival of ruin.

II

The willow drank the pelting stream
Lipped by the goat at Lampsacus,

And on Phaeacian bedrock
Nausicaä bruised the chaste cestus,
And the woodlands were the fane of Diana.
In the Asopus and Maeander
The virgin sang water-songs
And the Naiad showed her breasts
Hurt with untaken milk and love.
Ulai was the pooled threshold
Where holy Gabriel stood by Daniel;
But no angel sighs or messenger's intimations
To a spiky catfish or sea cow in the *da Prata*
Pouring its fresh furies for three leagues
Into the ocean.

Hercules and Father Liber cared for the vine, the fallow,
the ladle, and the wine-lees that nurse savine; Hesiod went
to the holm oak for honey, and Zeus plucked up dane wort
and hemlock to heal the crop. The droppings of the thrush
enlivened the furrow.

The Indies breeds no pining sorrow or domestic lament.
Nueva Firma maddens the wit, drives the faculty to pasture
with the pard, the mountain cat and black poplar. The man
of the new world has a bison's brow, a jaguar appetite and
horse's bowels. His precepts are from the sumac, potherb,
nettle branch, and the *Platte*, not ancient law.

Indian virgins chew a plant until the juice flows wine;
balsam for pains is in the tree-bark scratched by wounded
animals seeking a poultice. The aboriginal beef is taken from
the sea heifer that grazes upon the mangrove tree.

This is battle earth, forest is god,
And the loaves, wine and simple are from the tree;
But no Tree of Good and Evil has here been planted;
And the stemmy rains and vapors of Peru and the
    equinox
Are as the mists that went up before Creation.

The four rivers of Eden tamed the plum and the tuber-apple, and the winds pecked the fruits and seeds, carrying them to the Sierras and the Andean slopes.

> The terebinth is Abraham's angelic branch;
> The desert tamarisk is Saul's humble umbrella;
> Samuel, God's olive,
> Feeds the kids in Ramah;
> The sibyl Deborah has a timbrel
> No heavier than a peck of lupines,
> Her skirts are an homer of apples,
> And her virgin petticoats an ephah of figs;
> Aaron's tunic is table linen for Jacob and Rachel;
> The springs in the Palmyra sands are Tamar's girdle;
> Shun not Rahab, for through her gates
> Are the shouting dates and palms of Jericho.

III

A hemisphere had slept like unknown John in the crypt at Ephesus, the cartographer's honey but civet to the bowels. It was Isabella's, cosmography beyond Ptolemy's ken, *Cipango's* hinder door; its plenteous fields were covered with the Indian yam, the vestal squill, a nuptial dessert in the pompion's mouth.

The Florida currents were seers, carrying the *ceiba* of the Antilles to Gomera, Norway, and the Orkneys. The tunnies that victual near the Pillars were intimations of a double fortune.

> Western waters ran as April rivers,
> The tern, frigate bird and weed tangled with cane, berries, and ground-fruit
> Wrung God from lips demon'd by woeful sea-salt.
> But the race of men is bloat with boast,
> And cunning in fast and vigil.

Touching the Antilles the voyagers gave sighing appella-
tions to Indies' towns, bays and coves in homage to the As-
sumption, the petrine saint and undefiled Mary. Aaron's rod
nor Santiago James cast more prodigies than *Terra Firma*.

Rivers were salt at the mouth, a net brought up a sea pig,
and rumor disclosed unicorns and monkeys with a human
countenance. Cocoa-bodied Adams of flat faces swam with
parrots to the boats; girls of lissomy nakedness, wives with
but a clout, embalmed the island air, and so woo'd Cristobal
Colon he showed the savage cinnamon, pepper, pearl and
gold, and breathing vice and dropping water for the rood,
was sent left to leeward for ore in *Bohio*.

Plato's Atlantis had no gentler clime than *Española*. A
calabash of its soft waters were enough to content the soul
were it not that mountainous Pariacaca casts up the heart. On
its summit an Indian beat his body against the earth for un-
reasoned sorrow.

Plants trammelled with dew
And ground in greenstone,
Plucked from a cock's maw,
Heal the desponding spaces
That send men's thoughts downwards to Tartarus.
Onion in honey is a simple for tumorous dreams
That wear away youth
And of a sudden bring sunset to the head.
A plaister of dragon's blood,
Juice of nettles and osier root
Ease the mind bereft of its destiny.

Canopus, the Fisher,
And the mastic at *Puerto Santo*
Fetch an Ave Maria.
A mullet leaped into the pinnace;
Ilex and myrtle were Cordova's own,
But the river from *Sierras de Moa*

With the margaseta stones
Shone as Ophir.

When Colon's ship was aground a savage arrived with a
gourd of tears his king had shed.

Women, carrying calabashes of yams, hake, dory, gilt head,
accompanied by men, trembling for no hurt but affection,
approached the carracks in the river. The air, mild with aloes,
arbutus, cedar, the sweet reeds, cane of *Española* and the
tortoise, so affected Cristobal Colon that he named the harbor
Puerto de la Concepcion. The morrow was the vigil of *Santo
Tomas*, and he gave as tender another island to the Apostle.

Two girls, white as of Aragon, wore yellow grains in their
noses, and a cacique brought gold leaf the size of a hand. The
soil was guileless, but there are plants in the head, dodder
and bindweed, that ravish vetch; axe grass beheads the lentil;
the sparrow, a freebooter, will avoid millet if the ground be
the barrow of the toad.

Colon, of a turnip nose cropping up from the ruddle face,
was no robber Sisyphus; nor had Tantalus dowered him in the
race's genius, insatiate of seizing seas and fruits, even in
Erebus.

In *Española* the cacique had sent a mask with ears to porch
rumor, and the nose, gross with trade and old with proverbs,
was wrought of the ore that draws from the face lumps of
greed. The sailors filled their casks with water from the *Yaqui
River*, but only small gold adhered to the hoops.

Could he appear with begging leg before the Lady of the
earth with only a jakish title to squash, maize, and the potato,
heathen fellow in the furrow with Pythagoras's bean?

Devout Isabella was mortal, but goodness has a twin visage.
My Lady, of the space of a blush from Mary, has two breasts,
only one tender of hearing. She would heed how a king
brought three fat geese and cotton, or strain to her the sea
cow in the *Rio del Oro* that carries in an arm the infant
suckled, and would turn aside to wipe compassion from her
bosom. But with no caravel of cloves, without gold, and

proffering her twelve Turk Indians in stoles embroidered
with owls, she would press her hand to the other breast and
feel a stone.

> Hermes arrives on a sudden,
> But fate is slow, cannot be woo'd;
> Nor haste, nor wrath, nor leafy-filip
> Will make it otherwise blow.
>
> The earth rests upon the water
> Which bears the title Ocean,
> But Cristobal Colon has discovered a fistula of cockles.
> He shook the dross of origin,
> And imagined he was a cubit more of mortal dust.
> Madeira had been gained, Ombrion too,
> And this is St. Colon's day.

Am I, apprentice to Ptolemy, Isidorus, and King Juba, to
commence a new evangel of geography, and walk the earth
like forged knowledge? What Colchis have I found: The
world tempted Origen who shore away the man in him as
any sea dog would. What with a pippin face to vie with
Anaximander and Hipparchus, with the genius to gill the
cowslip, could I surmise a sea-vein to Ceylon where rice-
winds are the summery prayers at St. Thomas's burial stone?
I could have farmed a humble destiny besides two sons at
Cordova.

> Zama is the borning-town of Augustine,
> And Utica Cato's end.
> Sargon was a gardener in Sumer
> When Ishtar loved him,
> But the Admiral of the Seas, vowing a candle,
> Six pounds of wax in weight,
> To the Virgin of Guadalupe,
> Is a uterine Jew.
>
> The sun is good, the earth is dear, how then was
>   Golgotha?
> O Atlantic grief, I die nonentity.

Maybe no; Salt Oceanus is my deity,
And the murex that empurples the saints and
    Agrippina
Cannot live in fresh water.

There is a stygian dropsy sinks the blood;
The undyked spleen reduces all to gnome;
Had one a millenial pear in view
It would give the eye the gorgon's hue.
The sparhawks promise of Azores,
The wild asses laughing at Teneriffe,
Were woe and skull.

Let men cease their boast or lore be sere,
Caulk the boat and cast the Galilean weir.

Beatrice is the mother of Colon's sons. Accolade for Messalina who outranked her handmaiden in the Roman sport. Shame admonishes the polyp's head when coupling; the camel is a bride that goes privy to desert to rut.

Carnage and avarice tumor conscience, letting guile be its mummer. The tumulus at Oxhead was for Alexander's charger: elephant and baboon's milk are table for the Æthiopic at Apollo: at Sygaros seaweed and brine are toxin to the proscribed dog that is king in an Afric town. Negrana, Nesca, Masugum and Mariva were destroyed by Ælius Gallus who disclosed to the Romans that Araby Nomads take wine from the palm-tree and oil from sesame. The turtle-eaters, clothed in skins of fish, roof the marriage-house in the jocund shell of the tortoise. Ptolemais, Pharoah's hunting-ground, and Persepolis, were demolished by Alexander, yet in remembrance they ease the ravished faculty.

Shrive my soul if I decoyed natural lineage;
Cape Verde green by name is horrid sterile;
At Scoria the amber grows.
I thought to stock Nativity, Indies entire,
With mares, sow, the jack,
As the Kassite brought the horse to Ur.

I carried my intellect in a salver
It made my eye so dote,
Yet I knew man is issue of Balaam's ass,
And the Lampsacus goat.

Blow Etesian gales
Dividing two summery harvests at the westerly Indus.
Go soft to fate;
The Inca treads a bridge of straw.
Suffer darkness;
In antarctic October, night is king three hours.
O grief without asylum,
That shame can be no more sunk
Than the camel on the Dead Sea.
Let it not purloin the mind,
Ransacked by remorse,
Gibbering its guilt in asphodel.
Quiet, and erect thy towers at Gerra
Of squares of salt.

PART TWO

The hemisphere utters double inceptions;
Morning rains are as the moisture when Void ruled God,
And the tree clumps expel mists
Existing before the Lord divided the seas
And came to self-knowledge.

Custom is mocked: the canoe the savage plies on the river resembles the shuttle of the loom, but he weaves not; Mandioca looks meek as lentil, though it may kill. The Brazil sow goes with the loathly navel on its back; the tapir pastures at night. Sea calves and hog grow in ocean or swamp. Salt winds exhale health and longevity, but the Sertão brings mortal fevers.

Go not in the rain with Tlaloc,
Water-god dear to the infant pod,
Or close by the tapir, mule-nosed venery,

Or shores treaded by the sandpiper,
And the hawk that sends autumn.
Stubble and the deserted fallow are less false;
Ashes comfort the Sierra tree
And tenderly odor the sage;
Small herbs of stony places
And the turquoise placed between dead Mayan lips
Yield the breath of fate,
And millennial seasons older than Ocean.

Beat the green spined fruit on mountain stone,
Shun the evening toad
And plants that mire the hand.
The vine by the *Cupul Seas* sheds grapes
Before its foliage;
Wait for the galled leaves to quench the fox,
And cast them into the eagle's eyrie;
Let them not hatch.
Bloodstone is for desire
And the gods of the crossed rushes;
The curried crocodile softly woos *Tixzula*,
Her petticoat is an empurpled membrane,
And her blouse a white spire.
Unsourced sadness genders willowy streams,
And grows as poverty that feeds the tooth.
The jasper serpent drinks the pith of turtle-doves
And ravens upon the timorous deer
That has a hoof of venery chipped from the lava of
    Fuego.

Tolteca, blood-gatherers, planters of the skulled calabash from whose dew the Maid conceived Cakchiquel.
Chichimeca Tulán was your mother and father, and Quet-
zalcóatl your prophet. His name is Kukulcan, and he made
you a carver of the emerald, a sorcerer in silver, and for sky
he gave you a green gourd to seethe maize.
The artisan gathered cedar to shape the idols, sat by the
incense brazier, abstaining from salt, peppers and his wife,

and extirpated wanton images. A dancing crone robed in feathers gave admonitory blows on the knuckles of boys and vestals to inculcate veneration for the spindle, pounding maize, and gathering oysters in the *Champotón*.

Chaste water for the idols was brought from forests untouched by the skirt or hempen sandal of a *Chichén Itzá* maid. The Indian Chac sat humble on his mat burning copal, pouring wine and incense into the brazier, and sacrificing a captive, wounded in the secret parts, with whose blood he anointed the idols. A hedgehog of reedy arrows tipped with fish teeth were loosed at the victim, and an incision between the left nipple and the rib was made; and the living, embered heart torn out.

The embalmer at Crocodile passed the brain through the nostrils to preserve the mummy; the Mayans, showing that good and hurt are in the bowels, drew them out of the adulterer's navel.

Though the youths ravened upon the harlot, the vestal-cloth at *Chichén Itzá* was not despoiled. The virgin of *Cozumel* and *Mayapán*, of an herbal skin and gentler thigh than the women of Andalusia, turned to the side of the road when passing a man. She raised fowls, ground maize without tying up the breasts and had milk for the infant and for the nuzzling deer.

Chichimeca wanderer,
The stones and the ravine abhorred you,
The bat tore your head,
The crocodile slew your foot,
And the lava mountain peeled your lips;
When you lost the sacred corn-seed
The Tulán gods gave,
The smell of the points of the *ceiba* staff
Was your putative bread.

The desert took your hope,
And the waters by Acallan was lake sorrow.
The root and the tree were cankered;

Skilled in famine,
You ate the mellow innards of the Kunché bark
When Alvarado flailed the cocoa
And the maize fields.
At *Chi-Pixab* the mountain is named *Cakchiquel;*
He is a red tree;
Ever a forest and lava tribe,
Guatemala was the tree home.
Weaving, spinning, the grinding-stone were yours;
The Quiché was a seer of sea towns,
The Itzá at *Petén* were sculptors
Forefathered at Saïs, Memphis, Ur, Carthage.
You were a trader at *Xicalango,*
A boat-merchant on the *Chixoy,*
A water-child of *Usumacinta.*
Uxmal was the handiwork of Tutul-Xiu
And the stones of *Mayapán*
Were wrought by the lapidary Kukulcan.
When you were sojourners at *Panuco,*
You had gemmed the turquoise for centuries.
You had sacral writings,
Your Balam, the prophet, was the jaguar,
And all your annals came out of his ensanguined jaw.

Don Fernando entered the lagoons of *Dos Bocas* and
founded *Mérida. Campeche, Cozumel, Champotón,* and the
Sierra opposite *Mayapán,* contained idols and oratories that
kindled Christian rages. At *Campeche* a temple stood in the
sea and on its top steps sat a stone idol whose flanks two
animals were devouring. The pyramids of *Chichén Itzá* and
Mayapán were a seasoned art and experience to match a
Memphis or an Elephantine, and were groves for Baalim in
the valley of Hinnom.

Majuelas wrecked in Ascension Bay, and half dead, ate
snails and shell fish, and climbed a tree from which he
watched a tiger meal upon a deer, and when morning
came he ate what the tiger left.

Between *Campeche* and *Champotón* and the headland *Los Diablos* are low ranges, and when Francisco Hernández de Córdoba landed he called the place *Cape Cotoch* which means Our Houses.

There was a land white of earth,
Stones tempered by the equinox,
But good for Guatemala houses,
And grass that bosomed maize for millenniums.

The Adelantado Cortez provided Pedro de Alvarado with eighty horses, two hundred foot soldiers, much gun-powder and four field pieces of artillery, enjoining him to interdict man-eating and sodomy. The Christian expedition founded Guatemala at *Iximche* in 1524, and the Indians showed great fear of the first horses.

Quicksilver corrupts iron and copper,
But is unfevered and impotent in the ass's skin.
Mortal mien is no humble gourd;
Guatemala cast down Alvarado's gullet
Is not the water-fowl that gnawed the heart of the whale
That swallowed it.

O Quiché Maya—
The Pleiads and the herbs sowed a gentler visage
Weaning you from the Sierra and volcanic rock.
The maize nib and first sprouts vined the blood,
And the Jaguar-balam,
Yoked for planting the corn-seed,
Hymned the first mists
That begat mud-gendering men.
Then wood bare a man dry of cheek and hand,
And woman of wild rushes.
But the head fell to the side,
Soulless vessel too feeble to look back
Which is remembering.

Your face was morning,
And of virgin stone your teeth,
The eyes of the maid emerald,
When fate sent immortals,
Skin of white flowers,
Bodied of an animal
Sprung from the rising sun.

Children of Chichimeca,
Cotton was your raiment,
But the macaw made you vain,
The puma from the hills taloned your tribes.
The quetzal feather fell upon the virgin breast
Which seeded the Aztec mother of the war-god
Who was the first son of the Quiché Maya idols,
Mad for copal and the blood-flowing dance.

Take the conch,
Strike the burial-sounding tortoise
That draws the eyelid down;
Heed the *Xahila* plaint in the perished Maya tongue;
Lament the vestal,
She wore white earth,
Girdled with the maize-bud,
Fragrant with purslane, amaranth,
The potato and the cocoa tree.
Her sons and daughters were spindled pines;
Utlatlan was a giant cane lying to the South Sea;
She bore Quiché Maya.
Iximche, spurious issue of Castile,
Was overthrown by natural shakings.
Cuzcatlan, Mopicalco, Tacuylula are slain secrets
Furrowed in the gorge and plateau,
But the alum, sulphur and copper mountains,
Alvarado's gunpowder, remain.

PHOTOGRAPHING THE REALITY OF THE ABSTRACT

BEAUMONT NEWHALL

There are two courses open to the photographer. He can make the uncommon common. Or he can make uncommon the common.

The classic example of the photographer who aims to make the uncommon common is the news photographer. His goal is not to record the ordinary and the everyday, but the extraordinary and the unusual. Wherever there is disaster, the newsman is there. If he cannot find disaster, he searches for the odd and the peculiar, the exotic, and the unfamiliar. His photographs, seen by millions, make momentary events and strange occurrences all over the world our common property. What more striking evidence could be offered of this power of photography than the atom bomb? The mushroom cloud, the very symbol of nuclear fission, has become known through photographs.

This documentary aspect of photography was brilliantly presented in the winter of 1955 by Edward Steichen at the Museum of Modern Art, New York, in an exhibition titled "The Family of Man." The purpose of the exhibition was to restore man's faith in his neighbor by showing that all over the world he has the same reactions. Only photography could

161

bring together point by point visual comparisons of people doing the same things all around the earth. Again and again in this dramatic and spectacular display we were shown that everywhere the love-light of youth is the same, that everywhere motherhood is expressed in the same way, that children play and men laugh and weep and struggle and die in the same way.

There is another function which photography can play: to make uncommon the common. This, of course, is the way of the painter. Time and place, so all-important to the documentary picture maker, are of less interest to these cameramen. We are not concerned with their work as representational and objective, but as visually stimulating and subjective. Not that which is shown, but how the photographer has looked at the world about him is the simplest way to describe this approach.

It would be oversimplifying the problem to divide these two approaches into illustration on the one hand and concern with form on the other. The documentary photographer does more than illustrate, and the photographer, whom we must call for lack of a better term "pictorial," does more than record form. But still such a distinction makes clear the difference between the two.

The pictorial photographer is tempted to invade the territory that rightfully belongs to the painter. There is a long and often dreary tradition in the history of photography of the misuse of camera, lens, and light-sensitive material to emulate what is better done with brush, pigment, and canvas. Almost a hundred years ago, Henry Peach Robinson, imitating by the most skillful and ingenious techniques the genre and moralistic paintings of the Victorian period, set a style by precept and dictum. His book, *Pictorial Effect in Photography* had an enormous influence. When Impressionism gained acceptance, photographers followed, taking their cameras out-of-doors and focusing unsharply in an attempt to eliminate detail and compose by masses. And more recently the pioneers of abstract painting (themselves strongly influenced by objective photographs taken for scientific and recording purposes) pointed out a path which subjective photographers found almost irresistible.

In their enthusiasm for the ideals of the abstract painter a

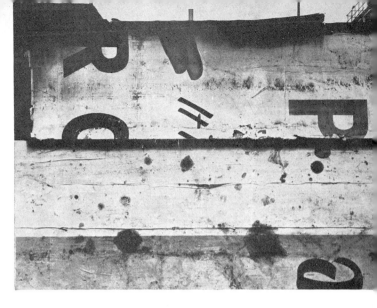

AARON SISKIND

school of avant garde photographers began to degrade the
medium by forgetting that what they were working with was
the camera and light-sensitive material. They laid heavy hands
upon the delicate detail which a lens naturally records. By
darkroom tricks they coarsened edges already precisely rendered. They deliberately invited bad processing so that the
silver grains which form the image would clump together,
creating a pebble-like over-all pattern. They even melted the
gelatin emulsion until it sagged and drooped, distorting the

AARON SISKIND

image which it bore. Or they forsook the lens entirely to create designs directly on sensitized paper by placing upon it objects both opaque and translucent.

The heydey of this co-called "experimental" photography was 1929, when a great photographic exhibition, "Film und Foto" was held in Stuttgart by the Deutsche Werkbund. Today the style is moribund. We have learned much about photography and much about painting. It is realized that it is wasteful for the photographer to emulate the painter. How rooted the "Film und Foto" exhibit was in the discipline of painters can be judged by the fact that an art historian, reviewing the exhibition in a photographic magazine, found no difficulty in pigeon-holing the photographs on display in three categories of painting: Expressionism, Abstraction, and the New Objectivity. The work shown at Stuttgart which

MINOR WHITE

today remains memorable was largely contributed by Americans: Edward Weston and his son Brett, Edward Steichen, Charles Sheeler and Berenice Abbott.

They, with others, notably Alfred Stieglitz, Paul Strand and Ansel Adams, were already formulating an approach to photography which had no name but was loosely called "straight" or

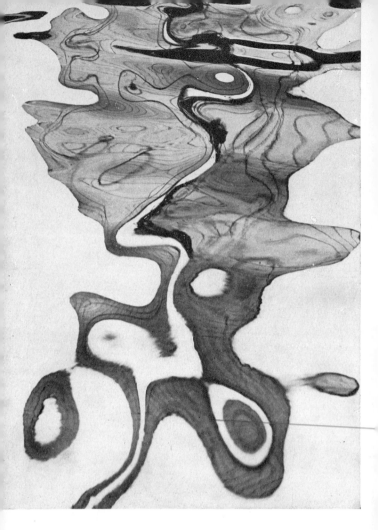

SIEGFRIED LAUTERWASSER

"purist." It was a functional esthetic. Since the camera image can contain infinite detail, let the negative, they said, be sharply focused and the print be of the same size on smooth paper. Since time can be stopped in its tracks by using fast film, let us explore the unseen attitudes of objects and beings in mo-

AARON SISKIND

tion. Since the camera finder or the ground-glass focusing screen isolates segments of the world, let us move in closely, to isolate details. But no esthetic can be purely mechanistic. Behind these constantly reiterated, technical criteria lay an awareness, which seldom became articulate, that photography has a psychological basis different from other picture-making ways.

The photographic image implies authenticity. How often have we heard the cliché: "The camera does not lie." We know that it does, outrageously so, yet we refuse to believe common sense. Someone was there, we feel, behind the camera when the shutter clicked and the exposure was made. And the resulting picture contains an amount of detail which

167

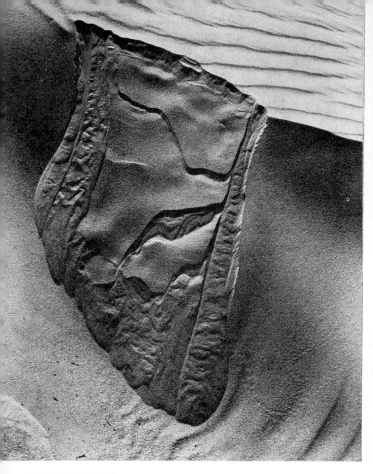

BRETT WESTON

could not be duplicated by the human hand. In the wealth
of detail there is almost always something with which we are
familiar, perhaps the mere texture of rock or weathered wood.
From there we go on to believe that which we cannot understand.

Detail in a photograph also plays a psychophysical role.
The reduction of a part of the natural world to a rectangle
of fairly small dimensions serves as a device to heighten our
perception. As we look about us, our eyes constantly rove,

BRETT WESTON

scanning the scene. In the photograph no such exertion is needful; though we do not take in the picture at a single glance, still the action of scanning is much less. The classic photographers of the straight approach have all preferred the 8 x 10 inch print size, which fully reveals detail, yet can be

MINOR WHITE

comfortably seen. Furthermore, they mount these prints on white boards with wide borders to isolate the image.

A painting may be of intrinsic value for its surface texture. The quality of the pigment, the evidence of the artist's hand in the drag of the brush or the troweling of the palette knife, play an important role in our appreciation of a painting. In photography any surface texture is an intrusion, and any attempt to emulate what is basic to the painter's craft by imposing a texture is bound to fail.

Form is basic to all art. The painter creates form; the photographer can only recognize it—unless he chooses to arrange objects in space for the purpose of photographing them, and then his skill lies in his ability to arrange, and the camera becomes simply a recording machine. Photographers endowed with a creative, visual imagination recognize form everywhere, even in the most common of objects. If they have sufficient skill, the form dominates the picture, arresting our imagination and compelling us to experience it. Here the photographer runs a course parallel to the painter. But, almost instantaneously, the spectator demands to know *what* is represented in the photograph, because he is so conditioned by the millions of factual photographs that he has seen. The painting, by its texture and calligraphy, provides us with sensuous beauty which is self-sufficient and, so to speak, carried by the form. The photograph leads us directly back to the world, for (if it is an honest photograph) it contains many clues to recognition. Thus we do not expect a photograph to be an *object* of beauty; rather, it is an experience which can be enjoyed over and over. Someone with eyes keener than ours saw form in what we have passed by a thousand times. Someone has made uncommon, and very special, the common. Our perceptions are sharpened. And if this experience can be linked with other experiences, by the train of associations set off by the form as well as the content, our emotions may be aroused. Alfred Stieglitz called some of his photographs "Equivalents" because to a remarkable degree they had this stimulating, catalytic effect upon the spectator.

When the photograph is rooted in reality, abstract form becomes functional. It sends us back to the world visually refreshed and stimulated.

FOUR DRAWINGS BY
FREDERICO GARCIA LORCA

DEATH

SELF PORTRAIT IN NEW YORK

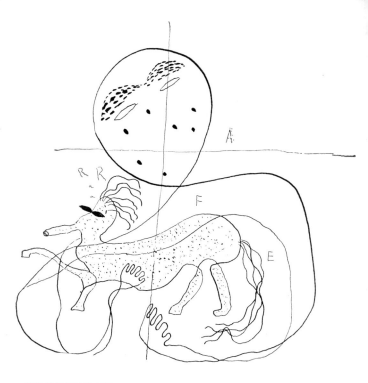

SELF PORTRAIT

RITUAL DANCE

VILLON'S WIFE

DAZAI OSAMU

translated by Donald Keene

I was awakened by the sound of the front door being flung
open, but I did not get out of bed. I knew it could only be
my husband returning dead-drunk in the middle of the night.

He switched on the light in the next room and, breathing
very heavily, began to rummage through the drawers of the
table and the bookcase, as if he were searching for something. After a few minutes there was a noise that sounded as
if he had flopped down on the floor. Then I could hear only
his panting. Wondering what he might be up to, I called to
him from where I lay, "Have you had supper yet? There's
some cold rice in the cupboard."

"Thank you," he answered in an unaccustomedly gentle
tone. "How is the boy? Does he still have a fever?"

This was also unusual. The boy is four this year, but
whether because of malnutrition, or his father's alcoholism, or
sickness, he is actually smaller than most two-year-olds. He is
not even sure on his feet, and as for talking, it's all he can do
to say "yum-yum" or "ugh." Sometimes I wonder if he is not
feeble-minded. Once, when I took him to the public bath

177

and held him in my arms after undressing him, he looked so small and pitifully scrawny that my heart sank, and I burst into tears in front of everybody. The boy is always having upset stomachs or fevers, but my husband almost never spends any time at home, and I wonder what if anything he thinks about the child. If I should mention to him that the boy has a fever, he says, "You ought to take him to a doctor." Then he throws on his coat and goes off somewhere. I would like to take the boy to the doctor, but I don't have any money. There is nothing else I can do but lie beside him and stroke his head.

But that night, for whatever reason, my husband was strangely gentle, and for once asked me about the boy's fever. It didn't make me happy. I felt instead a kind of premonition of something terrible, and cold chills ran up and down my spine. I couldn't think of anything to say, so I lay there in silence. For a while there was no other sound but my husband's furious panting.

Then there came from the front entrance the thin voice of a woman, "Is anyone at home?" I shuddered all over as if icy water had been poured over me.

"Are you at home, Mr. Otani?" This time there was a somewhat sharp inflection to her voice. She slid the door open and called in a definitely angry voice, "Mr. Otani. Why don't you answer?"

My husband at last went to the door. "Well, what is it?" he asked in a frightened, stupid tone.

"You know perfectly well what it is," the woman said, lowering her voice. "What makes you steal other people's money when you've got a nice home like this? Stop your inhuman joking and give it back. If you don't, I'm going straight to the police."

"I don't know what you're talking about. I won't stand for your insults. You've got no business coming here. Get out! If you don't get out, I'll be the one to call the police."

There came the voice of another man, "I must say, you've got your nerve, Mr. Otani. What do you mean we have no business coming here? You really dumbfound me. This time is serious. It's going beyond the limits of a joke when you steal other people's money. Heaven only knows all my wife and I have suffered on account of you. And on top of everything else you do something as low as you did tonight. Mr. Otani, I misjudged you."

"It's blackmail," my husband angrily exclaimed in a shaking voice. "It's extortion. Get out! If you've got any complaints I'll listen to them tomorrow."

"What a revolting thing to say. You really are an out-and-out scoundrel. I have no alternative but to call the police."

There was in his words a hatred so terrible that I went goose-flesh all over.

"Go to hell," my husband shouted, but his voice had already weakened and sounded hollow.

I got up, threw a wrap over my nightgown, and went to the front hall. I bowed to the two visitors. A round-faced man of about fifty wearing a knee-length overcoat asked, "Is this your wife?" and, without a trace of a smile, faintly inclined his head in my direction as if he were nodding.

The woman was a thin, small person of about forty, neatly dressed. She loosened her shawl and, also unsmiling, returned my bow with the words, "Excuse us for breaking in this way in the middle of the night."

My husband suddenly slipped on his sandals and made for the door. The man grabbed his arm and the two of them struggled for a moment. "Let go or I'll stab you!" my husband shouted, a jackknife flashing in his right hand. The knife was a pet possession of his, and I remembered that he usually kept it in his desk-drawer. When he got home he must have been expecting trouble, and the knife was what he had been searching for.

The man shrank back and in the interval my husband, flapping the sleeves of his coat like a huge crow, bolted outside.

"Thief!" the man shouted and started to pursue him, but I ran to the front gate in my bare feet and clung to him.

"Please don't. It won't help for either of you to get hurt. I will take the responsibility for everything."

The woman said, "Yes, she's right. You can never tell what a lunatic will do."

"Swine! It's the police this time! I can't stand any more." The man stood there staring emptily at the darkness outside and muttering as if to himself. But the force had gone out of his body.

"Please come in and tell me what has happened. I may be able to settle whatever the matter is. The place is a mess, but please come in."

The two visitors exchanged glances and nodded slightly to one another. The man said, with a changed expression, "I'm afraid that whatever you may say our minds are already made-up. But it might be a good idea to tell you, Mrs. Otani, all that has happened."

"Please do come in and stay for a while."

"I'm afraid we won't be able to stay long." So saying the man started to remove his overcoat.

"Please keep your coat on. It's very cold here, and I don't have any heating in the house."

"Well then, if you will forgive me."

"Please, both of you."

The man and the woman entered my husband's room. They seemed appalled by the desolation of what they saw. The mats looked as though they were rotting, the paper doors were in shreds, the walls were beginning to fall in, and the paper had peeled away from the storage closet, revealing the framework within. In a corner were a desk and a bookcase—an empty bookcase.

I offered the two visitors some torn cushions from which the stuffing leaked, and said, "Please sit on the cushions—the mats are so dirty." And I bowed to them again. "I must apologize for all the trouble my husband seems to have been causing you, and for the terrible exhibition he put on tonight, for whatever reason it was. He has such a peculiar disposition." I choked in the middle of my words and burst into tears.

"Excuse me for asking, Mrs. Otani, but how old are you?" the man asked. He was sitting cross-legged on the torn cushion, with his elbows on his knees, propping up his chin with his fists. As he asked the question he leaned forward toward me.

"I am twenty-six."

"Is that all you are? I suppose that's only natural, considering your husband's about thirty, but it amazes me all the same."

The woman, showing her face from behind the man's back, said, "I couldn't help wondering when I came in and saw what a fine wife he has, why Mr. Otani behaves the way he does."

"He's sick. That's what it is. He didn't use to be that way, but he keeps getting worse." He gave a great sigh, then continued, "Mrs. Otani. My wife and I run a little restaurant near the Nakano station. We both originally came from the country, but I got fed-up with dealing with penny-pinching farmers, and came to Tokyo with my wife. After the usual series of hardships and breaks, we managed to save up a little and, along about 1936, opened a cheap little restaurant catering to customers with at most one or two yen to spend at one time for entertainment. By not going in for luxuries and working like slaves, we managed to lay in quite a stock of whiskey and gin. When liquor got short and plenty of other drinking establishments went out of business, we were able to keep going.

"The war with America and England broke out, but even after the bombings got pretty severe, we didn't feel like being evacuated to the country, not having any children to tie us down. We figured that we might as well stick to our business until the place got burnt down. Your husband first started coming to our place in the spring of 1944, as I recall. We were not yet losing the war, or if we were we didn't know how things actually stood, and we thought that if we could just hold out for another two or three years we could somehow get peace on terms of equality. When Mr. Otani first appeared in our shop, he was not alone. It's a little embarrassing to tell you about it, but I might as well come out with the whole story and not keep anything from you. Your husband sneaked in by the kitchen door along with an older woman. I forgot to say that along about that time the front door of our place was shut every day, and only a few regular customers got in by the back door.

"This older woman lived in the neighborhood, and when the bar where she worked was closed and she lost her job, she often came here with her men-friends. That's why we weren't particularly surprised when your husband crept in by the kitchen door with this older woman, whose name was Aki-chan. I took them to the back room and brought out some gin. Mr. Otani drank his liquor very quietly that evening. Akichan paid the bill and the two of them left together by the back door. It's odd, but I can't forget how strangely gentle and refined he behaved that night. I wonder if when the devil makes his first appearance in somebody's house he acts in such a lonely and melancholy way.

"From that night on Mr. Otani was a steady customer. Ten days later he came alone and all of a sudden produced a hundred-yen note. At that time a hundred yen was a lot of money, more than two- or three-thousand yen today. He pressed the money into my hand and wouldn't take no for an answer. 'Take care of it please,' he said, smiling timidly. He looked as if he had already been drinking quite a bit, but, as you know, no man can hold his liquor like he can. Just when you think he's drunk, he suddenly becomes serious and engages in a perfectly rational conversation. No matter how much he drinks I have never seen him unsteady on his feet. They say that a man around thirty is in the prime of life and can hold his liquor best, but it is very rare to find anyone like Mr. Otani. That night he seemed to have drunk quite a bit before he came, and at my place he downed ten glasses of gin as fast as I could set them up. All this was almost entirely without a word. My wife and I tried to start a conversation, but all he did was to smile rather shamefacedly and nod vaguely. Suddenly he asked the time and got up. 'What about the change?' I called after him. 'That's all right,' he said. 'I don't know what to do with it,' I insisted, to which he smiled wryly and said, 'Please save it until the next time. I'll be coming back.' He went out. Mrs. Otani, that was the one and only time that we ever got any money from him. Since then he has always put us off with one excuse or another, and for three years he has managed without paying a penny to drink up all our liquor almost without assistance."

Before I knew what I was doing I burst out laughing. It all seemed so funny to me, although I can't explain why. I covered my mouth in confusion, but when I looked at the lady I saw that she was also laughing unaccountably, and then her husband could not help but laugh too.

"No, it is really no laughing matter, but I'm so fed up that I feel like laughing. Really, if he used all his ability in some other direction, he could become a cabinet minister or a Ph.D. or anything else he wanted. When Akichan was still friends with Mr. Otani she used to brag about him all the time. First of all, she said, he came from a terrific family. He was the younger son of Baron Otani. It is true that he had been disinherited because of his conduct, but when his father, the present baron, died, he and his elder brother were to divide the estate. He was brilliant, a genius in fact. In spite of his youth he was the best poet in Japan. What's more, he was a great scholar, who had gone from the Peers' School to the First High School and the Tokyo Imperial University. He was a perfect demon at German and French. To hear Akichan talk, he was a kind of god, and the funny thing was that she didn't make it all up. Other people also said that he was the younger son of Baron Otani and a famous poet. As a result even my wife, who is getting along in years, was as wild about him as Akichan. She used to tell me what a difference it makes when people have been well brought up. And the way she pined for him to come was quite unbearable. They say the day of the nobility is over, but until the war ended I can tell you that nobody had his way with the women like that disinherited son of the aristocracy. It was unbelievable how they fell for him. I suppose it was what people would nowadays call 'slave mentality.'

"For my part, I'm a man, and at that a very cool sort of man, and I don't think that some little peer—if you will pardon the expression—some member of the country gentry who is only a younger son, is all that different from myself. I never for a moment got worked up about him in so sickening a way. But all the same, that gentleman was my weak spot. No matter how firmly I resolved not to give him any liquor the next time, when he suddenly appeared at some unexpected hour, looking like a hunted man, and I saw how relieved he was at last to have reached our place, my resolution weakened, and I ended up by giving him the liquor. Even when he got drunk he never made any special nuisance of himself, and if only he had paid the bill he would have been a good customer. He never advertised himself and didn't take any silly pride in being a genius or anything of the sort. When Aki-chan or somebody else would sit beside him and sound off to us about his greatness, he would either change the subject completely or say, 'I want some money so I can pay the bill,' throwing a wet blanket over everything.

"The war finally ended. We started openly doing business in black-market liquor and put new curtains in front of the place. For all its seediness the shop looked rather lively, and we hired a girl to lend some charm. Then who should show up again but that damned gentleman. He no longer brought women with him, but always came in the company of two or three newspaper and magazine writers. He was drinking even more than before, and used to get very wild-looking. He began to come out with really vulgar jokes, which he had never done before, and sometimes for no good reason he would strike one of the reporters he brought with him or would start a fist-fight. What's more, he seduced the twenty-year-old girl who was working in our place. We were really dumbfounded, but there was nothing we could do about it at that stage, and we had no choice but to let the matter drop. We advised the girl to resign herself to it, and quietly sent her back to her parents. I begged Mr. Otani not to come any more, but he answered in a threatening tone, 'People who make money on the black market have no business criticizing others. I know all about you.' The next night be showed up as if nothing had happened.

"Maybe it was by way of punishment for the black-market business we had been doing that we had to take such a monster on our hands. But what he did tonight can't be passed over just because he's a poet or a gentleman. It was plain robbery. He stole 5,000 yen from us. Nowadays all our money goes for stock, and we are lucky if we have 500 or 1,000 yen in the place. The reason why we had as much as 5,000 yen tonight was that I had made an end-of-the-year round of our regular customers and managed to collect that much. If I don't hand the money over to the wholesalers immediately, we won't be able to stay in business. That's how much it means to us. Well, my wife was going over the accounts in the back room and had put the money in the cupboard drawer. He was drinking by himself out in front but seems to have noticed what she did. Suddenly he got up, went straight to the back room, and without a word pushed my wife aside and opened the drawer. He grabbed the 5,000 yen in bills and stuffed them in his pocket.

"We rushed into the shop, still speechless with amazement, and then out into the street. I shouted for him to stop, and the two of us ran after him. For a minute I felt like screaming 'Thief!' and getting the people in the street to join us, but after all Mr. Otani is an old acquaintance, and I couldn't be too harsh on him. I made up my mind that I would not let him out of my sight. I would follow him wherever he went, and when I saw that he had quieted down, I would calmly ask for the money. We are only small business people, and when we finally caught up with him here, we had no choice but to suppress our feelings and politely ask him to return the money. And then what happened? He took out a knife and threatened to stab me! What a thing to happen!"

Again the whole thing seemed so funny to me, for reasons I can't explain, that I burst out laughing. The lady turned red, and smiled a little. I couldn't stop laughing. Even though I knew that it would have a bad effect on the proprietor, it all seemed so strangely funny that I laughed until the tears came. I suddenly wondered if the phrase "the great laugh at the end of the world" that occurs in one of my husband's poems didn't mean something of the sort.

And yet it was not a matter that could be settled just by laughing about it. I thought for a minute and said, "Somehow or other I will make things good, if you will only wait one more day before you report to the police. I'll call on you tomorrow without fail." I carefully inquired where the restaurant was and begged them to consent. They agreed to let things stand for the time being, and left. Then I sat by myself in the middle of the cold room trying to think of a plan. Nothing came to me. I stood up, took off my wrap, and crept in among the covers where my boy was sleeping. As I stroked his head I thought how wonderful it would be if the night never never ended.

My father used to keep a stall in Asakusa Park. My mother died when I was young, and my father and I lived by ourselves in a tenement. We ran the stall together. My husband used to come now and then, and before long I was meeting him at other places without my father's knowing it. When I became pregnant I persuaded him to treat me as his wife, although it wasn't officially registered, of course. Now the boy is growing up fatherless, while my husband goes off for three or four nights or even for a whole month at a time. I don't know where he goes or what he does. When he comes back he is always soused, and he sits there, deathly pale, breathing heavily and staring at my face. Sometimes he cries and the tears stream down his face, or without warning he crawls into my bed and holds me tightly. "Oh it can't go on. I'm afraid. I'm afraid. Help me!"

Sometimes he trembles all over, and even after he falls asleep he talks deliriously and moans. The next morning he is absent-minded, like a man with the soul taken out of him. Then he disappears and doesn't return for three or four nights. A couple of my husband's publisher-friends have been looking after the boy and myself for some time, and once in a while they bring enough money to keep us from starving.

I dozed off, then opened my eyes before I was aware of it to see the morning light pouring in through the cracks in the shutters. I got up, dressed, strapped the boy to my back and went outside. I felt as if I couldn't stand being in the silent house another minute.

I set out aimlessly and found myself walking in the direction of the station. I bought a bun at an outdoor stand and fed it to the boy. On a sudden impulse I bought a ticket for Kichijoji and got on the tram. While I stood hanging from a strap I happened to notice a poster with my husband's name on it. It was an advertisement for a magazine in which he had published a story called *François Villon*. While I stared at the title *François Villon* and at my husband's name, painful tears sprang from my eyes, why I can't say, and the poster clouded over so I couldn't see it.

I got off at Kichijoji and, for the first time in I don't know how many years, I walked in the park. The cypresses around the pond had all been cut down, and the place looked like the site of a construction. It was strangely bare and cold, not at all as it used to be.

I took the boy off my back and the two of us sat on a broken bench next to the pond. I fed the boy a sweet potato I had brought from home. "It's a pretty pond, isn't it? There used to be many carp and gold fish, but now there aren't any left. It's too bad, isn't it?"

I don't know what he thought. He just laughed oddly with his mouth full of sweet potato. Even if he is my own child, he did give me the feeling almost of an idiot.

I couldn't settle anything just by sitting there on the bench, so I put the boy on my back and returned slowly to the station. I bought a ticket for Nakano. Without thought or plan, I boarded the tram as though I were being sucked into a horrible whirlpool. I got off at Nakano and followed the directions to the restaurant.

The front door would not open. I went around to the back and entered by the kitchen door. The owner was away, and his wife was cleaning the shop by herself. As soon as I saw her I began to pour out lies of which I did not imagine myself capable.

"It looks as if I'll be able to pay you back every bit of the money tomorrow, if not tonight. There's nothing for you to worry about."

"Oh, how wonderful. Thank you so much." She looked almost happy, but still there remained on her face a shadow of uneasiness, as if she were not yet satisfied.

"It's true. Someone will bring the money here without fail. Until he comes I'm to stay here as your hostage. Is that guarantee enough for you? Until the money comes I'll be glad to help around the shop."

I took the boy off my back and let him play by himself. He is accustomed to playing alone and doesn't get in the way at all. Perhaps because he's stupid, he's not afraid of strangers, and he smiled happily at the madam. While I was away getting the rationed goods for her, she gave him some empty American cans to play with, and when I got back he was in a corner of the room, banging the cans and rolling them on the floor.

About noon the boss returned from his marketing. As soon as I caught sight of him I burst out with the same lies I had told the madam. He looked amazed. "Is that a fact? All the same, Mrs. Otani, you can't be sure of money until you've got it in your hands." He spoke in a surprisingly calm, almost explanatory tone.

"But it's really true. Please have confidence in me and wait just this one day before you make it public. In the meantime I'll help in the restaurant."

"If the money is returned, that's all I ask," the boss said, almost to himself. "There are five or six days left to the end of the year, aren't there?"

"Yes and so, you see, I mean—oh, some customers have come. Welcome!" I smiled at the three customers—they looked like workmen—who had entered the shop, and whispered to the madam, "Please lend me an apron."

One of the customers called out, "Say, you've hired a beauty. She's terrific."

"Don't lead her astray," the boss said, in a tone which wasn't altogether joking. "She cost a lot of money."

"A million dollar thoroughbred?" another customer coarsely joked.

"They say that even in thoroughbreds the female costs only half-price," I answered in the same coarse way, while putting the sake on to warm.

"Don't be modest! From now on in Japan there's equality of the sexes, even for horses and dogs," the youngest customer roared. "Sweetheart, I've fallen in love. It's love at first sight. But is that your kid over there?"

"No," said the madam, carrying the boy in her arms from the back room. "We got this child from our relatives. At last we have an heir."

"What'll you leave him beside your money?" a customer teased.

The boss with a dark expression muttered, "A love affair and debts." Then, changing his tone, "What'll you have? How about a mixed grill?"

It was Christmas Eve. That must be why there was such a steady stream of customers. I had scarcely eaten a thing since morning, but I was so upset that I refused even when the madam urged me to have a bite. I just went on flitting around the restaurant lightly as a ballerina. Maybe it is just conceit, but the shop seemed exceptionally lively that night, and there were quite a few customers who wanted to know my name or tried to shake my hand.

But I didn't have the slightest idea how it would all end. I went on smiling and answering the customers' dirty jokes with even dirtier jokes in the same vein, slipping from customer to customer, pouring the drinks. Before long I got to thinking that I would just as soon my body melted and flowed away like ice cream.

It seems as if miracles sometimes do happen even in this world. A little after nine a man entered, wearing a Christmas tricornered, paper hat, and a black mask which covered the upper part of his face. He was followed by an attractive woman of slender build who looked thirty-four or thirty-five. The man sat on a chair in the corner with his back to me, but as soon as he came in I knew who it was. It was my thief of a husband.

He sat there without seeming to pay any attention to me. I also pretended not to recognize him, and went on joking with the other customers. The lady seated opposite my husband called me to their table. My husband stared at me from beneath his mask, as if surprised in spite of himself. I lightly patted his shoulder and asked, "Aren't you going to wish me a merry Christmas? What do you say? You look as if you've already put away a quart or two."

The lady ignored this. She said, "I have something to discuss with the proprietor. Would you mind calling him here for a moment?"

I went to the kitchen, where the boss was frying fish. "Otani has come back. Please go and see him, but don't tell the woman he's with anything about me. I don't want to embarrass him."

"So he really has come after all?" The proprietor had half doubted my lies, and yet he seemed nevertheless to have placed quite a bit of trust in them. Now he simply had concluded that my husband had returned as the result of some instigation on my part.

"Please don't say anything about me," I repeated.

"If that's the way you want it, it's all right with me," he consented easily, and went outfront. After a quick look around the restaurant, the boss walked straight to the table where my husband was. The beautiful lady exchanged two or three words with him, and the three of them left the shop.

It was all over. Everything had been settled. Somehow I had believed all along that it would be, and I felt exhilarated. I seized the wrist of a young customer in a dark-blue suit, a boy not more than twenty, and I cried, "Drink up! Drink up! It's Christmas!"

In just thirty minutes—no, it was even sooner than that, so soon it startled me, the boss returned alone. "Mrs. Otani, I want to thank you. I've got the money back."

"I'm so glad. All of it?"

He answered with a funny smile, "All he took yesterday."

"And how much does the rest of what he owes you come to altogether? Roughly—an absolute minimum."

"Twenty thousand yen."

"Does that cover it?"

"It's a minimum."

"I'll make it good. Will you employ me starting tomorrow? I'll pay it back by working."

"What! You're joking!" And we laughed together.

Tonight I left the restaurant after ten and returned to the house with the boy. As I expected, my husband was not at home, but that didn't bother me. Tomorrow when I go to the restaurant I may see him again, for all I know. Why has such a good plan never occurred to me before? All the suffering I have gone through has been because of my own stupidity. I was always quite a success at entertaining the customers at my father's stall, and I'll certainly get to be pretty skillful at the restaurant. As a matter of fact, I received about 500 yen in tips tonight.

From the following day on my life changed completely. I became light-hearted and gay. The first thing I did was to go to a beauty parlor and have a permanent. I bought cosmetics and mended my dresses. I felt as though the worries that had weighed so heavily on me had been completely wiped away.

In the morning I get up and eat breakfast with the boy. Then I put him on my back and leave for work. New Years is the big season at the restaurant, and I've been so busy my eyes swim. My husband comes in for a drink about once every two days. He lets me pay the bill and then disappears again. Quite often he looks in on the shop late at night and asks if it isn't time for me to be going home. Then we return pleasantly together.

"Why didn't I do this from the start? It's brought me such happiness."

"Women don't know anything about happiness or unhappiness."

"Perhaps not. What about men?"

"Men only have unhappiness. They are always fighting fear."

"I don't understand. I only know I wish this life could go on forever. The boss and the madam are such nice people."

"Don't be silly. They're grasping country-bumpkins. They make me drink because they think they'll make money out of it in the end."

"That's their business. You can't blame them for it. But that's not the whole story is it? You had an affair with the madam, didn't you?"

"A long time ago. Does the old guy realize it?"

"I'm sure he does. I heard him say with a sigh that you had brought him a seduction and debts."

"I must seem a horrible character to you, but the fact is that I want to die so badly I can't stand it. Ever since I was born I have been thinking of nothing but dying. It would be better for everyone concerned if I were dead, that's certain. And yet I can't seem to die. There's something strange and frightening, like God, which won't let me die."

"That's because you have your work."

"My work doesn't mean a thing. I don't write either masterpieces or failures. If people say something is good, it becomes good. If they say it's bad, it becomes bad. But what frightens me is that somewhere in the world there is a God. There is, isn't there?"

"I don't have any idea."

Now that I have worked twenty days at the restaurant I realize that every last one of the customers is a criminal. I have come to think that my husband is very much on the mild side compared to them. And I see now that not only the customers but everyone you meet walking in the streets is hiding some crime. A beautifully dressed lady came to the door selling sake at 300 yen the quart. That was cheap, considering what prices are nowadays, and the madam snapped it up. It turned out to be watered. I thought that in a world where even such an aristocratic-looking lady is forced to resort to such tricks, it is impossible that anyone alive has a clear conscience.

God, if you exist, show yourself to me! Towards the end of the New Year season I was raped by a customer. It was raining that night, and it didn't seem likely that my husband would appear. I got ready to go, even though one customer was still left. I picked up the boy, who was sleeping in a corner of the back room, and put him on my back. "I'd like to borrow your umbrella again," I said to the madam.

"I've got an umbrella. I'll take you home," said the last customer, getting up as if he meant it. He was a short, thin man about twenty-five, who looked like a factory worker. It was the first time he had been a customer since I was working in the restaurant.

"It's very kind of you, but I am accustomed to walking by myself."

"You live a long-way off, I know. I come from the same neighborhood. I'll take you back. Bill, please." He had only had three glasses and didn't seem particularly drunk.

We boarded the tram together and got off at my stop. Then we walked in the falling rain side by side under the same umbrella through the pitch-dark streets. The young man, who up to this point hadn't said a word, began to talk in a lively way. "I know all about you. You see, I'm a fan of Mr. Otani's and I also write poetry myself. I was hoping to show him some of my work before long, but he intimidates me so."

We had reached my house. "Thank you very much," I said, "I'll see you again at the restaurant."

"Goodbye," the young man said, going off into the rain.

I was wakened in the middle of the night by the noise of the front gate being opened. I thought that it was my husband returning, drunk as usual, so I lay there without saying anything.

A man's voice called, "Mrs. Otani, excuse me for bothering you."

I got up, put on the light, and went to the front entrance. The young man was there, staggering so badly he could scarcely stand.

"Excuse me, Mrs. Otani. On the way back I stopped for another drink and, to tell the truth, I live at the other end of town, and when I got to the station the last tram had already left. Mrs. Otani, would you please let me spend the night here? I don't need any blankets or anything else. I'll be glad to sleep here in the front hall until the first tram leaves tomorrow morning. If it wasn't raining I'd sleep outdoors somewhere in the neighborhood, but it's hopeless with this rain. Please let me stay."

"My husband isn't at home, but if the front hall will do, please stay." I got the two torn cushions and gave them to him.

"Thanks very much. Oh, I've had too much to drink," he said with a groan. He lay down just as he was in the front hall, and by the time I got back to bed I could already hear his snores.

The next morning at dawn without ceremony he took me.

That day I went to the restaurant with my boy as usual, acting as if nothing had happened. My husband was sitting at a table reading a newspaper, a glass of liquor beside him. I thought how pretty the morning sunshine looked, sparkling on the glass.

"Isn't anybody here," I asked. He looked up from his paper. "The boss hasn't come back yet from marketing. The madam was in the kitchen just a minute ago. Isn't she there now?"

"You didn't come last night, did you?"

"I did come. It's got so that I can't get to sleep without a look at my favorite waitress's face. I dropped in after ten but they said you had just left."

"And then?"

"I spent the night here. It was raining so hard."

"I may be sleeping here from now on."

"That's a good idea, I suppose."

"Yes, that's what I'll do. There's no sense in renting the house forever."

My husband didn't say anything but turned back to his paper. "Well, what do you know. They're writing bad things about me again. They call me a fake aristocrat with Epicurean leanings. That's not true. It would be more correct to refer to me as an Epicurean in terror of God. Look! It says here that I'm a monster. That's not true, is it? It's a little late, but I'll tell you now why I took the 5,000 yen. It was so that I might give you and the boy the first happy New Year in a long time. That proves I'm not a monster, doesn't it?"

His words didn't make me especially glad. I said, "There's nothing wrong with being a monster, is there? As long as we can stay alive."

A SELECTION OF FRENCH POEMS

translated by Kenneth Rexroth

I WILL TAKE YOU

RENE-GUY CADOU

I will take you across my saddle
I will take you or if you want I will take you
Like a fine woolen caparison
  Over my horse I will take you

I will take you from your family
I will take you from the window where you smiled
I will take you from your shell
  Sweet pearl of night.

I will take you like a long bath drawn out
So slowly all a summer afternoon
I will take you from where you hide high in the leaves, my
    dove
  I will take you I will go

I will go to countries we don't know
Across unknown autumnal forests

Hand on the shoulder of my horse
  Like a little angry bird

I will go I will have you better at the end of the road
Some morning in the great solitude of the fields
You will slip between my knees like a spring
  I will take you I will go

THE SHADOW

FRANCIS CARCO

When I waited for you in the bar
That night amongst the drunks
Who snickered when they tried to laugh,
It seemed to me that you came late,
And that somebody followed you in the street.
I saw you look around before you came in.
You were afraid. You closed the door.
And your shadow stayed outside.
It was that which had followed you.

Your shadow is always in the street,
Near the bar where I waited for you so often.
But you are dead.
And your shadow ever since is in the doorway.
And wherever I go now, it follows me,
Fearfully, like a beast.
If I stop, it stops.
If I speak to it, it runs away.

Your shadow is the color of rain,
Of my regrets, of time which passes.
It may disappear and hide itself,
But when night comes, it is everywhere.

At the subway station La Chapelle,
In the poor and clamorous slums,

It waits for me behind the black pillars,
Where other fraternal shadows
Wave to the passersby and call
With great gestures of hopelessness.

But the passersby never turn around.
Not one has ever known why,
In the wind which makes the street lamps blink,
In the cold wind, full of mystery,
Suddenly they quicken their steps.

And I, who seek where you might be,
I, who know that you wait for me there,
I pass without recognizing you,
I come and go all night,
I walk alone, just like in the old days,
And your shadow, the color of rain,
Driven at each step by the wind,
Your shadow is lost in the night,
But I feel it all about me.

When you were just a street walker,
Just an innocent prostitute,
Like the girl who appeared
In Whitechapel
One night, to Thomas De Quincey,
And whom he sought, too late, and never found,
From doorway to doorway and hotel to hotel—
As he tells in a book.

It was there, for the first time, that I met you.
You were tired and sad, like the tarts of London.
Your hair still held an odor of fog.
And while they stood you drinks,
The drunken longshoremen insulted you,
Or went home with you in the sombre street.

I never forgot the effect which you had on me,
In that hopeless book.

Nor the wind, nor the rain, nor the gleaming pavement,
Nor the murderers of the night,
Nor the flares of the coffee stalls,
Nor the eddies of the Thames,
Between its dismal embankments.
Now, after all those years,
Another who resembles you
Comes, along the grey buildings,
Beckons to me and accosts me.

It is not you. It is everything which you call back to me.
As I was sad before I knew you,
As I sank down with pleasure in my sorrow,
Walking the streets, going into the bars,
Begging the shadows of the night to speak to me,
Wandering on and on without stopping—

But everywhere it was too late.

The music of an accordion breaks off with a cough.
They take down the lights one after another.
A passerby from whom I ask a light
Holds out to me a dead cigar.

Wherever I turn my steps it is the same story.
I am always going toward the train whistles,
On a great boulevard troubled and peopled with ghosts.
There I wait for I do not know who, I do not know why—
But the trains pass screaming,
And this waiting is more like leaving.

You have come to go away,
I have brought you to these desolate places,
And you have said to me, "Whatever you do,
It is me, from now on, you will see among all these ghosts.

You will feel me near you.
You will think that I am dead.
And you will never forget me."

I listened to you and followed you under the streetlights.
There was no one but us alive where we went.
Only us, but I knew that of the two of us, the first
To say goodbye would be you.
There is no use trying to
Hold you by your little hand.
The cries, the rumbling, the smoke of the trains,
The rails and their signal lights,
The black bridge all resounding,
The noise of the heavy boxcars bumping each other,
By an obscure foreboding have already separated us.

Another time, in the same sinister district,
We seat ourselves on a bench in the night.
And the wind which drives the rain,
The lamps of the rooming houses,
The pimps in their damp sweaters,
The girls who stare at us,
Gather around us, their witches'
Circle draws in on us.
Then you are put to tears,

Trying to explain to me, without raising your voice,
That one day you will deliver me
From these ghosts who are in me—
You talk and the rain falls.
It is the rain which makes you weep,
With a grief which nothing can appease,
With an inconsolable pain.

And the round of shadows and of the lights of houses
Revolves tirelessly
With the guys and their girls,
The bars where the jukeboxes grind,
Flinging to us sometimes through the door
The call of a dead voice—

The round which nothing can stop,
Turns and carries me with it, with you who are dead,

Turns and will carry me always, with all my past,
Out of time, out of the world, out of all that is
Or is not, as you, in the shadow, you know——

NYMPHE LIMINAIRE

RENÉ DAUMAL

A corpse wanders in the hallways;
Look at me here, here where I can't even see daylight.
Here the ghost can materialize,
Here take on those tragic airs,
And if you want to have fun in the passageways,
Beware! Beware!
And if you rock in your rocking chair
Beware! Beware of the little girl
With her scraps of fog,
With her hands, with her transparent rags,
She crams your mouth
And you stifle
And you collapse on the sofa. . . .
I don't want to remember but it is always there
All the scenes I imagine
I find them again with a clot of blood at the corner of the lips,
A corpse prowls, beware!
A corpse who shrinks from hour to hour
Hung from your neck, a rag,
      As the saying goes, a lock
Which shuts you up in the deepest dungeon.

EPITAPH

ROBERT DESNOS

I lived in those times. For a thousand years
I have been dead. Not fallen, but hunted;
When all human decency was imprisoned,
I was free amongst the masked slaves.

I lived in those times, yet I was free.
I watched the river, the earth, the sky,
Turning around me, keeping their balance,
The seasons provided their birds and their honey.

You who live, what have you made of your luck?
Do you regret the time when I struggled?
Have you cultivated for the common harvest?
Have you enriched the town I lived in?

Living men, think nothing of me. I am dead.
Nothing survives of my spirit or my body.

LAST POEM
—*Terezina Concentration Camp May 1945*

ROBERT DESNOS

I have dreamed so much of you,
Walked so often, talked so often with you,
Loved your shadow so much.
Nothing is left me of you.
Nothing is left of me but a shadow among shadows,
A being a hundred times more shadowy than a shadow,
A shadowy being who comes, and comes again, in your sunlit
    life.

YOU WILL BE NAKED

FRANCIS JAMMES

You will be naked in the parlor among the old things,
Slim as a reed spindle of light,
And, legs crossed before the rosy fire,
        You will listen to the winter.

At your feet, I will take your knees in my arms.
You will smile, more gracious than a willow branch,

And, laying my hair against your sweet thighs,
      I will weep because you are so good.

It will be good for us to be proud of each other.
And when I kiss your throat, you will kiss
My eyes, and smile at me, and bend
      Your gentle neck.

Then, when the old servant, ill and faithful,
Raps on the door and says, "Dinner is served,"
You will start, and blush, and your slender hand
      Will adjust your grey robe.

And while the wind comes under the door,
And the worn clock strikes the wrong time,
You will put your legs, perfumed of ivory,
      Back in their little black cases.

LEGEND

MICHEL LEIRIS

Today the doors open by themselves
The locks can't sleep quietly in their obscurity
Calmer than a sea of oil

Great tapestries harnessed by the eyes of women
You collapse like a ripped cloud curtain
And unmask a sun which is only a woodpile of eyeballs

A deaf Inquisition terrified the room
Pincers of softened boards
Pillory of the table
Drowning of the ceiling
The scissors open wide their jaws
Like the yawns of an inconsolable widow
But their branches flung by chance

Cut only emptiness
A haggard emptiness that height itself has abandoned

The three logs turn to ashes in the chimney
The bed is open
And I see going out up to her waist from the shore
A woman undressed and beautiful
Who throws her torn-off clothes into the sea

Great proud face
It won't take you long to sink in the quicksand
Your locks themselves will not be saved
You vanish completely and the shore closes over you
And does not keep the exquisite odor of your body
Vapor of underground drunkenness
That might still have reached the nostrils of the universe
And seized the aerial time and depraved it

Only the clothes beat on the waves towards other slumbers

O breasts in soft flames and corpses swallowed by quicksand
The world lacks a burning pasture
To feed its enchanted herds.

VACANT LOTS

O. V. DE LUBICZ-MILOSZ

How did you come to me, o you so humble, so sad? I no longer
    know.
Probably like the thought of death, in the midst of life.
But, from my ashen Lithuania to the hellgate of Rummel,
From Bow Street to the Marais, and from childhood to old
    age,

I love (like I love mankind, with an old love,
Worn with pity, anger and solitude) these forgotten places,

Where sprouts, here too slowly, here too quickly,
Like white children in sunless streets, a weed

Of the city, cold and soiled, sleepless as an obsession,
Come with the wind from the cemetery perhaps
In one of those bolts of black cloth, smooth and shiny, pillows
For the old Sleepers of the Rocks, in the terrible twilights.

From my whole youth, wasted in the south
And the north, I have kept only this—my soul
Is sick, passing, like a thirsty wallflower
Which has been picked and forgotten and left here.

I know one more shadowy than a cedar of Lebanon! The
    vestige
Of a beautiful garden of virginal love. And I myself know
    that holy tree
Was planted there, long ago, one balmy day, at last
To bear witness; and the word fell into mute eternity;

And the nameless man and woman are dead, and their love
Is dead, and who remembers them now? Who? You, perhaps,
You, sad, sad, sound of rain on rain—
Or you, my soul. But soon you will forget this and every-
    thing else.

And the other, where the great wind and rain and mist are
    their church.
When winter comes to the slums, when the barge
Travels through the fogs of France, how good it was,
St. Julian the Poor, to walk

In your garden. I have lived in the bitterest
Dissipation. But already the heart of the earth
Was drawing me, and I knew that it beat, not under
The carefully tended rose bushes, but where my sister the
    nettle flourished, obscure and broken.

And so, if you wish to please me, afterward, far away! You
Murmuring, streaming with reborn flowers, you, garden
Where all loneliness has a face and a name
And will be a mate,

Do not walk on the mossy wall where crevices
Reveal the city, Ariel, in the pure clouds,
For my bitter love, a friendly corner of cold, mildew
And silence, and when the Virgin with Thummim and Urim
    on her breasts

Takes me by the hand, and leads me there, how the sad
    earthly people
Will remember, will recognize me, will welcome me, the
    thistle and the high
Nettle, and belladonna the enemy of childhood.
Those, they know, they know.

THE SAME NUMBER

PIERRE REVERDY

The wide-open eyes
      The hand on the other shore
The sky
      And everything that happens there
The leaning door
      A by-passed head
In a frame
And through the shutters
You can see across
      The sun fills everything
But the trees are always green
      The falling hour
      It gets warmer
And the houses are smaller
The passersby go less quickly

And always look up
> The lamp shines on us now

Looking far away
We can see the light
> Coming

We will be happy
> This evening

At the other house where somebody waits for us.

MIRACLE

PIERRE REVERDY

Hanging head
> Curling eyelashes

Silent mouth
The lights go on
There is nothing there but a name
> Which has been forgotten

The door will open
And I won't dare go in
> Everything happens there

They talk
> And I can listen

My fate is at stake in some side room.

FALSE DOOR OR PORTRAIT

PIERRE REVERDY

> In the place which lies there

Between four lines
> A square where white plays

The hand which holds your cheek
> Moon

A face which lights
> The profile of another
>> But your eyes

I am the lamp guiding myself
Finger on damp eyelid
      In the midst
The tears flow in this space
      Between four lines
      Ice.

LATE AT NIGHT

PIERRE REVERDY

The color which decomposes the night
The table where they sit
In its glass chimney
      The lamp is a heart emptying itself
It is another year
      A new wrinkle
Would you have thought of it
      The window leans a blue square
The door is more familiar
      A separation
         Remorse and crime
Goodbye I am falling
Into the gentle bend of arms which take me
Out of the corner of my eye I can see them all drinking
      I don't dare move
They sit there
The table is round
And so is my memory
I remember everybody
Even those who are gone.

MEMORY

PIERRE REVERDY

Just a minute
      And I am back
With all those who have gone

I have kept nothing
Stop
> The swollen sky
> > And at the last moment
The lantern goes by
> The step you hear
When somebody stops and everybody else goes on
You let go the world
> And what is inside
Are dancing lights
> And an outstretched shadow
There is still space
> Looking ahead
And a cage where a live animal leaps
Breast and arms make the same motion
A woman was laughing
> With her head turned
And the person who came amazed us
We didn't know ourselves all three of us
> And yet we shaped
> > A world full of hope.

THE DRY TONGUE

PIERRE REVERDY

There is a nail
> Holding up the slope
The bright tatter of twisting wind blows and anyone who
> understands
> Everything is naked
The pavement the sidewalks the distance the railings are
> white
> > Not a drop of rain
> > Not a leaf of a tree
> > Not the shadow of a garment
> > I wait
> > > The station is a long way off

The river still flows between rising embankments
>The earth is dried out
>>Everything is naked and white
With only the movement of a clock out of order
>The noise of the train passed
>I wait.

SECRET

PIERRE REVERDY

>The empty bell
>The dead birds
In the house where everyone is asleep
>Nine o'clock

The earth holds itself immobile
>You would say somebody sighed
The trees look like they were smiling
>>Water trembles at the tip of each leaf
>>>A cloud crosses the night

In front of his door a man is singing
>The window opens noiselessly

THE WORLD BEFORE ME

PIERRE REVERDY

Some time ago
One clear night
A new sun arose
Next day
An old man kneeling held out his hands
Animals ran all along the road

I was sitting down
Dreaming

A window opened above my head
There was no one inside
A man passed behind the hedge

The field where a single bird sings
Somebody is afraid
It is amusing
Down there between two little children
Joy
You against me
The rain washes away our tears

You can't walk the narrow path
You come back the same way
But there is a barrier
Something has fallen
Down behind there
A shadow bigger than itself
Takes a turn around the earth
And me, I am still sitting here **afraid to look.**

THE HOT GIRL

R. V. CASSILL

Byron was lying on the porch glider reading *The Big Money* when the preacher and his wife arrived. He heard their feet on the concrete steps and before he turned over to face them he thought with lazy resentment, They've found us. They couldn't wait.

The small town afternoon was brutally hot, and for a couple of hours the edge of sunshine had moved toward him across the porch floor until finally when he rocked to the left, it lit up the corner of the glider. On that corner the glider frame had become too hot to touch. He saw from this that he would have to move soon, but he hated the preacher and his wife for disturbing him ahead of what he considered the natural time to leave his reading and speculating.

This was only the second day he had been in this town, coming home from his Freshman year at college after his parents had moved, and it struck him as pretty nice to be where you didn't know the neighbors and they didn't know you. The two days had been a mediocre idyl, as innocent and vacuous as the scratching of the vine leaves when they moved against the splinters of glass embedded in the kellystone wall.

"Afternoon, afternoon," the preacher said. His wife stood behind him grinning.

She was ugly enough to fit as a preacher's wife, Byron thought.

"Is the father home?"

What father? *Our* father?

"Dad," Byron yelled. He sat upright and pulled his T-shirt down to cover his stomach. "Won't you folks go right in? Dad and Mother must be in the front room."

"It's almost too hot," the preacher's wife said, and then jerked her head nervously as though she felt she shouldn't be the one to say such a thing.

Byron stared at her with mute hostility and then, as his father came to the door, rolled and squirmed back to the most comfortable position he could find for reading, back to the drugged, imaginative mood that was composed more of the licking heat and wind-sounds than of the book he was reading. But he read this weather into the pilgrimage of poor Charlie Anderson, tumble-weeding back and forth over the American spiritual desert.

He heard the preacher and his father talking inside and the subdued obbligato of the women's voices. Every awareness floated in the great washtub-pudding of what he called his *thinking about things*—Charlie Anderson, the red and blue glints on the kellystone wall and the pocks like navels where the glass bits had fallen out, Margo Dowling, the preacher's voice, Rodney Cathcart, the burned pasture down the hillslope, the stringy twitching of his belly.

"It's all there," he thought luxuriously. If he wanted to grab one thing out of the pudding for study or to play with, all he had to do was fish down. To play with the preacher, for instance, could spin out in a realistic drama that was kind of funny to think about now. He would bet the preacher was around drumming up trade for his church, and he had swooped on them because they were new in town. His father would fall for it, and about supper time his father would say to him with a phony innocence, "About time to get cleaned up a little, isn't it, boy?"

He would come back with just a little more innocence, "What for, Dad?"

"Why, why, didn't I tell you? The Christian minister specially invited us to come to services tonight."

Then his mother would say tightly, "Ralph, I don't think it's fair to force Byron to go. Maybe he doesn't think that way any more. Maybe he feels different."

"Force him? I only said . . ."

"I know. *I* think it would be all right if only you and I and Sarah Jean went. Then people couldn't say anything. They wouldn't think anything about it if Byron didn't come. Maybe it's against his *principles* to go to church."

By this time his father would be turning purple (and he couldn't say he blamed him much). "*Principles? Force him?* Oh *gracious* no! Is he too pure to step inside a church? I never heard of anyone else too pure to go to church. What is he? An *atheist?* A Robert Ingersoll? My God, I'm only suggesting this because we're new here in town and we want to do unto others and we ought to act a little *friendly.* . . ."

His mother would smile and nod ironically. "Friendly doesn't mean you can let other people tell you 'Oh, you have to think this; oh, you have to think that; oh, you have to come to my church and fold your hands and pray just like me.'" Her falsetto imitation would mock the Pharisees around about.

"I don't give a goddamn what friendly means! I'm only saying will he go to church tonight if he's not too PURE?"

That's just the way it would go, if he let it. Now that he had foreseen it all, why bother? Be big, he told himself cynically, Go to the Christian Endeavor meeting. You're not too pure. Go scare up some quiff.

He flicked over a number of pages so he could read the part about Margo Dowling while the urgent heat snuck onto the glider.

II

There were fourteen young people at Christian Endeavor, and they sat centered in the hot, wood-rot-smelling gloom of the church on the two benches directly in front of the pulpit. Now, in the late dusk, one of the diamonds of red glass still burned in the west window, and the island of girls in light dresses and of boys straining their throats to sing or nudging each other, hung compact as a group of pagan votaries celebrating the omnipotence of the blood. A basket of gladiolus, brought for the morning service, drooped softly in the heat around the yellow shaft of the podium.

Sniffing at her sweated powder, Byron decided his pitch was for the girl with the black hair and white dress. While they all sang *Though Your Sins Be as Scarlet* the girl, as though the song might be a curtain that hid her, kept peeping at him. Her eyes were dark, tapering to points at the outer corners. Her mouth caressed the song with little kissing pouts.

"God bless you and keep you. Amen," the preacher said. "Don't forget the ice-cream social Friday night. Like to have you all stay for the sermon now."

But they all left—either to go home or to wait in the cooler air outside until they would be joined by a handful of older folks for the second part of evening services.

Passing through the vestibule the black-haired girl rubbed Byron's arm and said "Whee-ew" enthusiastically. She touched her sweating forehead with dark-red fingertips and filled her lungs with the even air that met them at the outside door.

"Yeah," he said. "Yeah."

A car with a cutout passed on the main street, a block away. Its red taillights flew among the trees like scattering sparks. He could hear children shouting at an after-dark game.

"Say," He faced the girl squarely and watched her queerly squeeze her eyeballs with her lids and smile disdainfully at him. "May I take you home?"

"Mmmmm," she ran her tongue slowly across inside her lower lip. "I'm not going home *now.*"

"Whenever you go, I mean," he prepared himself to sit through the coming sermon if necessary.

"I have to go to the UB church and play for my mother. She's gonna sing. You can walk up there with me but don't if you don't want to. It wouldn't be any skin off me."

"Sure I want to."

"Really? Oooooo!"

As they walked along a dark sidewalk in a part of the little town he didn't yet know she said, "You don't know my name but I know yours. You're Byron Schwartz and you go to college. I knew a college boy once. Wowee! Well, I'm Ginger." She giggled for reasons of her own, and while he was trying to think of a reply he suddenly and surprisingly felt her fingers slip up to his armpit.

"Well, I'm ticklish," he said.

"Goody."

"Ginger Rogers?" he asked.

"No. I wish I was half as pretty as her. I'm just Virginia Burke. Ginger Burke."

Ahead of them the arched lights of church windows appeared and they heard the singing of the United Brethren like the lowing of goaded animals.

"I love nights. Any kind of nights," Ginger said. "I wish I didn't have to go in that hot hole. We won't stay long."

"Fine. Where do you live?"

"A long way," she said archly. "Clear past the edge of town. Out where the grass grows tall."

The church to which they had come was much smaller than the other one, but so crowded with the seated congregation that they had trouble finding seats. Exposed to the crowd-stares Byron had the first of his regrets that he had ever seen Ginger, but she seemed to joy in dragging him up and down the aisles and whispering loudly. She found them seats, finally, near the back. They sat beside a scowling old woman, whose eyes in a sagged face had the mean, agate look of a hawk's.

The sound of the preacher's voice now squealed and prayed through the packed room and Byron felt both excited and disturbed by it. It upset him that anyone should do such unnatural things with his voice, but that someone was doing it seemed to hint at licenses he had never been permitted or even told of. Ginger's shoulder and thigh were jammed tight against him and the skin of their forearms touched. He felt something rub the back of his leg and when he realized that it was the arch of her foot, a tough, pleased, dazzled assurance that he was going to get her settled like a crown on his brows.

Slyly she had reached her hand beneath both their adjacent arms to take his. In his damp palm her hand was dry, grainy, rubbery. She began to squeeze rhythmically, her hand performing that learned imitation of peristalsis that farmers use in milking. He submitted happily, passively, but after a little while she whispered, "Whassa matter with you? Squeeze back. Squeeze *back!*" He started to giggle nervously, but the stare of the old woman beside them quieted him.

"I've got to go now," Ginger said. "That's my mother. She's going to sing." As she slipped past him the gilded, crazy feeling collapsed, and for a moment he considered getting away before she came back—away into the cool of the night. The old woman kept staring hatefully at him.

He made an effort to listen to her accompany her mother's song. He told himself, as if that mattered, that neither Ginger or her mother ought to be allowed to perform in public. They were dismal. But he wanted her back beside him.

The song concluded the service. In the rising crowd he dodged swiftly away from the old woman, gauging his course so as to catch Ginger at the door. He watched her come toward him, but she was looking past him; her eyes, round with alarm, were fixed on something or someone outside on the church steps.

She did not pause at all when she came even with him, only turned her head down enough to hide the movement of her lips as she whispered, "M' boyfriend's out there. He'd kill us both. See you later." As if she were actually a creation of his overheated thoughts—or some nightmare that sprang from his being in a strange town—she disappeared. When he got up nerve to sidle out on the steps he saw no sign of her.

All the way home he kept wondering if she were real, and it had all been upsetting enough to scare him some with the thought that she might not be.

III

The ringing of the telephone the next morning penetrated his dream like a summons to rise and account for his guilty lusts of the night before.

While he lay there listening to his mother answer in the next room he knew—he told himself later that he had known—the call was for him and knew who was calling.

His mother smirked as he walked to take the phone from her hand, but he scarcely looked back at her.

"I have to see you," Ginger said.

"Never mind," he croaked nervously. "Just forget it."

"No, no. I *have* to. I'm down at the Post Office. You come *down*. You've got to."

"I've got to eat breakfast."

"No, no, no, no. *Now!*"

He looked once across the sun-white dining room and into the kitchen where his mother was already laying strips of bacon in the skillet for his breakfast. He groaned and ran out of the house, hearing his mother's voice diminish behind him, "Byron, boy, are you pretty hungry this morning?"

It was her skin that fascinated him as he stood beside Ginger in the Post Office. She was even better-looking in the daylight than he had thought when he first saw her the night before. Her arms, legs, neck, and, so far as he could tell, her breasts had a tight, swollen look. Her long, black hair sung on her shoulders alive as snakes. Her skin was odd, rather olive-colored, though just now its tight-drawn surface was misted with sweat so it had the acid-gold appearance of fly-paper.

For the benefit of the people who were picking up mail she pretended surprise at seeing him—another gambit he could not understand, for of course she had used the phone inside the postmaster's wicket and everyone in the room must have heard her call. She was hard at work addressing a post-card, and he leaned on the desk beside her. When he asked, as casually as he could, what was going on, she whispered dramatically, "Not here. Wait a sec." In a little while she took his hand and led him to a side street which, in the syrupy heat of the morning, was empty.

"I told him last night," she said. She turned to face Byron, so close that her breasts almost touched him. "I told him about *us*. I broke with him. He said he would kill himself, then he said he'd kill me. My boyfriend. Tell me I did right, Byron."

"What is there to tell him about us?"

"The way we feel, silly."

"Oh."

A truck with two farmboys riding in the bed swung around the corner and sprayed gravel into the dusty weeds in the ditch. The delicate, separate puffs of dust raised by the falling gravel went up separately into the barred light.

"O.K.," Byron said. "You told him."

"I love you, Byron. I honestly told him last night that since I'd met you I couldn't stand him any more. I wouldn't even let him touch me." She giggled. "He was so mad, because usually I do." Then her face, quick and easy as winking, took on an expression of wonder and suffering. "I can't stand it until you tell me that you love me too."

He shifted uneasily from one foot to the other, looked in her eyes, as brown and cloudy as an animal's. He looked at the shadow her dress strap threw on the skin of her shoulder. "What is love?" he said uneasily.

"*You know.*"

"O.K.," he said. "I do." She swayed toward him, recovered, and led him a few steps further before she turned.

"That's fine," she said. "Then I want you to come out this afternoon. Can you dance? I'll teach you. Come about one. Only Byron, if he—I mean if he should come to your house looking for you, don't even go out. He might kill you."

When he agreed to come to her place, he was making a surrender to a state of fantasy that would last through the week, and yet it was not pure lunacy for him to yield—he still knew, in a reserved corner of his mind, what was going on. Lying on the porch glider an hour after he had met her in the Post Office—his eyes not quite focusing on the maple leaves in front of them, he remembered their declarations of love with cynical amusement. Whatever weird things this dummy might think of next he would go along with, but without believing them quite real. He began to see that this unbelief was even a part of the pleasure she tempted him toward, an unreality that would give him a freedom he had never experienced except in dreams.

From here, looking back, it was almost as if, when he had changed buses at Des Moines on his way home from college, he had stepped through a wrong door and had been carried into a world that looked real enough and familiar enough at first, but which was actually shifted a quarter of an inch from reality so no chain of consequences seemed to work. His own thoughts took off now from this quarter inch of deviation, making him a spectator of whatever he might do. "I'll be damned," he whispered to himself. " 'Don't go out if he comes looking for you. He might ki-i-i-ill-ll-l you.' " The word kill seemed particularly ridiculous and tickling—as though in this atmosphere of strangeness it referred to nothing that could possibly happen to him.

"What are you chuckling about?" his mother asked. She had brought her sprinkling can to water the ferns ranked at the edge of the porch, but this work was only her excuse to be where she could talk to him. He knew she thought he had been avoiding her, that he hadn't shared with her as many of his thoughts as formerly.

"Ah, the world's a big farce," he said. "A big farce. People never know what they're up to themselves. You know—how they get involved in what they do. It's all a mystery, so why try to understand it?"

His mother shook her head. "Oh, I don't think that's necessarily so. I think if we approach things right and honestly try to do our best then we can work our problems out."

"Naa," he said. "It's hopeless, that's why it's all right. We're just puppets. 'Chemisms' like Dreiser says."

"I don't think he says *that*, does he?" his mother asked anxiously. " 'The world is within you,' " she quoted. "That means you can be just as fine a person as you want to."

"Hogwash," he said. "We're nothing but blind worms."

"Now where did you learn to be such a pessimist? That isn't learning. Our biggest men, like Einstein and John

Dewey think there's, perhaps, some hope for the world. If only we're patient with our fellowmen and don't throw ourselves away foolishly, why I think there's hope for a better world. I know there are bad men who think we're going to have a war, but we don't have to pay any attention to them."

"Naa. It's all crazy and that's all right. I'm not complaining."

"I know you're not," she said. She looked down at him rocking on the glider with such an overflow of love that it seemed it might suddenly rush down, entangle him, hold him safe and forever, horribly motionless. He wished that she would go away and let him think about this hot dolly Ginger. That seemed a dirty way of putting it, but he did not want his mother persuading him out of anything that might be coming his way.

"You mustn't just pessimistically throw yourself out of life's race," she said. "I don't know who that young lady was that called you up so early this morning. I guess it must have been someone you met just last night, and I expect she's a nice girl, but I do think it's a little funny she should be calling you up so soon. My goodness. I wouldn't want you to throw yourself away, I mean. Why don't you drive back to Davisburg and see Francine? I'll ask Daddy if you can have the car. You could stay with one of your friends, and . . ."

"I don't want to see Francine." She had been his girl in high school, and she was fine in her way, but she didn't seem worth the effort of going to Davisburg and there was no hope of getting anywhere with her unless she'd changed plenty since he saw her last.

"Well, I thought you always got along so nicely with Francine." His mother reached to stroke his hair and he squirmed at her touch. "Francine is a pretty girl," she said.

"So I know she's pretty. Have I got to go see her just because she's not a crow?"

His mother's lips trembled. "I can't always follow your *reasoning*," she said. Then she began her most devastating line. "I know we haven't given you as much *stability* as we should. It does seem that we're always moving from one town to another just when you've made friends one place. But it isn't fair not to stick to old friends. Francine . . ."

"Don't worry about it. You seem to think whatever I do is bad."

"Oh no. You're *good*. It's simply that I don't want you to throw yourself away on this girl when you're too young to know about life."

"But Mama, I'm *not*. I'm not throwing myself anywhere. Don't you understand?"

She would not be consoled. "There're a lot of worldly tricks you don't know about. Some women are tricky."

"I won't even be here long enough to get mixed up with her. You know that."

"That's another thing," his mother said. "I wish you'd give up this idea of hitchhiking clear out to California. You could stay around here, or if we bore you too much you could go back and get your job in Davisburg. Then you'd have time to read and think. You always tell us you want to be alone so you can read and think. You're too young to be tearing breakneck all the time. If you'd just stay here we'd try not to get on your nerves too much."

"I want to go to California," he said in exasperation, closing his eyes, hoping she'd leave him alone soon.

"I don't know why. Don't you think we worry when we know you're wandering around like some tramp?"

"I feel like I need to," was all he would reply to this. Then he simply refused to answer at all and she went away. Lying there, he shut his eyes and had such a spicy vision of Ginger as he had not yet allowed himself—to make up for the worry of being in a world where everyone wanted to nag at him.

But he managed no vision of her quite so troubling, withholding, promising, yielding as Ginger herself. That afternoon at her house first she took him into the parlor to dance. Her mother was busy in the kitchen and the baby sister was pretending to help her. They were only a step out of sight around the edge of the parlor door, and the way Ginger rubbed herself against him kept him nervous and afraid that her mother might step back and see them. Instead of holding

Ginger—instead of having to hold her—he leaned back in her strong arms and let her whirl him around. Whirling, getting dizzy in the heat, he saw the windows spin slowly, as though he were in a cistern and the windows were the far-off top through which he saw the sky.

"You aren't trying," Ginger said crossly.

"Yes I am."

"Well, give," she said and grabbed him again. He imagined then, not quite sure yet what it was she wanted him to try, that he might be an explorer at the world's edge, caught by a woman-shaped beetle that clutched him while he still dispassionately tried to study it. He felt that maybe he had become tiny enough so a common beetle could whirl him around as it pleased.

"You better try," she threatened again.

"What?" he asked desperately.

"Yeah," she said, grinding against him and letting him go. "Come in here. I want to show you some graduation presents." The next room was her bedroom and after she had led him there she began piling his arms full of boxes. Tissue paper rustled out of some of them, and from some came the smell of powder and perfumed things.

"Here," Ginger said, "isn't this darling?" A comb and brush. "This is sweet." A blue robe. "How do you like this?" She held a pair of panties to her body and seemed daring him to look down at them. She began to hum and wiggle. "Like it?" she said.

A small cardboard box fell from the top of the stack he was holding. He got very red and squatted to pick it up.

"Vir—JINNya," her mother called. "You come take Marilyn a while. She's in my way too much and you're not doing anything."

Ginger ran out of the bedroom, throwing something at his face as she ran. He carefully set down the boxes and got his shaking hands on what she had thrown. He had to hold it quite close to his eyes before it was clear to him that this was another pair of panties, yellow, with a green, embroidery script that said *Forget me not*.

The room had become a solid dream where he was lost and from which he would have to be led.

IV

"Do you want to go on, for gosh sakes, and play in the barn, Marilyn?" Ginger asked nastily. The little girl, who sat between them on the front steps refused to answer. She only turned her face to her sister with a grave, hurt stare.

"I said DO YOU WANT TO GO PLAY IN THE BARN MARILYN?" Ginger shook the child. "Well, you do whether you know it or not. We'll all go."

Since they lived a little past the edge of town, the Burke's place was something like a farm. There was an orchard of some size along the highway, a fenced lot where the cow pastured, and a barn much too big for any present use they had for it. Mr. Burke wasn't a farmer; he ran the lumberyard, Ginger said.

The big, cathedral-like barn had been put up before the farmland behind their place had been separated and sold. It was a tall, gray building full of rooms and corridors with ladders here and there going to the upper floors.

"Here's the oat bin," Ginger said. She led the two of them inside, knelt and picked up a handful of grains and let them go sliding through her plump fingers. "Wouldn't you just love to play here in the oats, Marilyn?"

"No-ooooh," Marilyn said.

"Now look here, sweetie, Byron and I are going to play upstairs and you'd be afraid to climb up there. YOU PLAY HERE NOW MARILYN."

"Don't want to."

"PLAY!"

Deftly she got Byron outside and locked the door of the bin on her little sister. They listened a minute to see if the child would cry, and when she didn't—she only seemed to be scratching at the door with her fingernails and crooning—Ginger kissed him and said, "Let's go."

Their progress through the barn was this: In each room she would throw herself on him, whining, muttering, dodging, and squeezing him breathless while they kissed. Intermittently she would peel her mouth from his to say, "I know you love me," or "I want to be yours, Byron—*Byron*, what a silly name," or "I didn't know love could be like this." In each room he attempted to wrestle her to the floor, but she was too strong and when he tried she would lead him to another room. Finally, they climbed into the high-roofed, empty haymow.

Pigeons flew out through the haymow door when they appeared. In this big space a kind of hush came over their feelings. It was simply too big to be appropriate for the kind of mush they had been talking; they were too insignificant under the broad arch of the roof to keep any intensity mustered.

Somewhere Ginger had walked through a cobweb and there was a smudge of dirt on the sweatslick of her forehead. She looked like a farm girl just come in from hoeing in the corn.

She stood leaning against the frame of the door, sulky, and after a while asked, "Was I dreaming? Or did you ask me to marry you?"

He put his arm around her and began to fondle her once more. "You weren't dreaming," he said tentatively.

"Can it be that I've only known you since last night? It seems forever. Don't do that, they can see."

"There isn't anyone out there to see."

"We've got to go let Marilyn out. She could smother in the oats or something."

"Will you come out with me tonight then?"

"I know what you mean," she said thoughtfully. "No."

"Why?"

"Oh Byron, I want to wait until we get married."

"To hell with it then."

"You mean—getting married?"

"I don't remember saying anything about that. I just went along with the gag."

Her lips pouted. She looked at him—not like a jilted girl, but like a very small one who has been cheated in a game by a rule-breaker.

"I'll bet you think I'm in love with love," she said.

This was too much for him and he burst out in a satisfying laugh. He sat in the door and swung his legs against the side of the barn. He watched the pigeons circle back toward the barn and veer off with swift, jerking wings. "Why don't you forget it? You've seen too many bad movies."

When she sat beside him her skirt came up well above her knee to where the skin was not gold-colored but white with the blue mark of veins in it. She watched him look at the leg.

"I know how we could manage," she said. "I don't think my folks would let me if I told them I want to marry you, but you say you're going to California, and I'll go too. They'll buy me a ticket and you can meet my train in Kansas City and we'll get my ticket changed so we can ride out in a compartment. I've got lots of money. Will you, Byron?"

He lit a cigarette and watched the match fall to the ground below them, spinning like a maple seed.

"I wouldn't do that," he said.

"I bet you want to go back to college instead of getting married. I bet you have a lot of fun with the college girls, huh?"

"Sure." He laughed bitterly, thinking that if he had, he wouldn't be making such a fool of himself now.

"I know what," she said. "You get your father's car tomorrow night."

"He won't let me have it."

"Get it. We'll go out and see what kind of a man you are."

That struck in his mind, not as ideas are supposed to strike, but surprisingly like an actual blow at the top of his spinal cord, with a blinding, hurting flash, and he saw her momentarily, swinging her white legs toward him, then gathering her feet under her to stand, through a haze fretted with red.

She ran then and kept running for the rest of the afternoon. She kept just out of reach as if daring him to grab her. When he went home at five he felt as though he had done a day's work.

Supper with his family was an ordeal, though he felt better afterward. About eight o'clock, when it was beginning to get dark, he called Ginger. He couldn't help it. After a hot, wrenching moment of hope while the phone rang, her mother answered and told him she had gone out riding. After he figured on that one a while both his anger and his sense of the ridiculous told him with whom she had gone.

v

It was late, probably two or three o'clock, and he had been lying on the porch roof a good long time with his arm thrown across his eyes to shut out the yellowed moonlight. After the crisis moment of the phone call he had gone to the edge of town and had run for a while—partly on his own silly initiative and partly because he remembered a lecture in which a minister had said that such exercise drove away the torment of impure thoughts. When his thoughts seemed funnier if not purer he returned to the house and tried writing a letter to Perry Klein, who was still back in Iowa City going to summer school.

"No sooner do I get home than I meet the most ridiculous quail," he had written. "In a church, no less. She acts hotter than a firecracker but I can't quite make her out or, I mean, make out with her . . . YET ! ! !" But he couldn't hold to the letter. A really bright plan lured him and he fancied it up.

He would keep on with Ginger, long enough to take her in the conventional fashion, and just before he did it he would give her some gum to chew—a gesture of his contempt, a sort of prophylactic measure that would keep her from becoming any serious responsibility of his. Really, that would protect him from any of the consequences that a guy could imagine. If the rubber should break, and he guessed such things happened, he wouldn't have to feel sorry for a stupe who would chew gum while she screwed. He could leave her laughing.

He went to bed with this thought, hoping it was good enough to put him to sleep. But it wasn't, quite. He tossed a great deal and thought of dying, as he too frequently did when sleep wouldn't come. He felt his pulse. Then he pushed open the window screen, looked both ways to make sure the maples would hide him from any neighbor or passer-by, and crawled out to lie naked in the clean wash of the moonlight.

With his arm across his eyes, taking the moonlight only on his goose-pimpling skin, he began to see the car, the heavy car, in which Ginger was riding with the killer boyfriend.

He saw them driving on a dirt road that swung through a shadowed valley and then, liberated, upon the wide bulge of a hill, rise to the very top—then sinking, pointing, falling in an immense glide into another valley whose cleft was furry with willows growing along a creek.

He was wholly with them—first above them like an eye from which they could not escape, next, becoming the killer himself, watching Ginger shrink from him at the far side of the seat.

The car was stopped among the willows. His shadow moved across the seat toward her. Moved closer until she lost the separate curves of feminine articulation and overfilled his sight the way a yellowed wall of ice might confront him when he got to the mountains. There was no real flesh to stop him, to thrust back and impede his desire with its counterlunges, and so his desire swept on through her to a brief, terrible vision of understanding, and he saw himself nakedly encountering the king, fear, and the glacier, wall, the infinity beyond his desire, in which he would be lost, nothing. He had in imagination passed through her as old pagans might have passed a natural gateway of stones to face and scream at the unknown landscape beyond and carry from that the strength to endure afterward. All of a sudden it seemed to him that he had to have her, and that from this challenge he dare not flee or allow himself to be driven. Either he must take her yielding for an armor or vulnerable go on from here.

At the end of his knowledge—as insight drained away like lust itself—he found himself trembling in frightened impatience to see her again. To see her and shape from her body the magic that would save his life.

VI

"I thought I told you to get your old man's car," Ginger said. "Whatsa matter? Wouldn't he let you have it? Then I won't either."

She was not at all in a good humor. She had gone to a lot of trouble to look nice for him when he came for her. Her hair was tied with a virginal bow; her mouth was spread with a rich paste of lipstick. And after all that he had appeared without a car. She snorted but agreed to go to the drug store for a coke.

On the way he fumbled an explanation, "The clutch isn't in very good shape."

She didn't believe this at all. "Whaaat? Ha! Can't you drive, either?"

"I can drive. What do you mean, *either?*"

"You sure can't dance. It's no *fun* to dance with you. I don't know what else you can do."

"You said you'd see. You will."

"Oh don't talk fresh."

"As a matter of fact Dad had to have the car tonight. That doesn't make any difference does it?"

"I'm certainly not going to walk out in the country with you," Ginger said.

At the drugstore they had their coke in hostile silence. A couple of boys Byron had seen on the street came in and began teasing Ginger by flipping water on her with the tips of their fingers. She seemed to get so much fun out of this, writhing and bouncing, that Byron was worried about how to get her away.

One of them put a piece of ice down her dress and she twisted so much in trying to get it out that the white-haired druggist yelled "Wheeee" in a tone that made all of them catch their breaths.

"Give me a pack of gum," Byron said to the druggist.

"Where's Carl tonight?" one of the boys asked Ginger.

"Never you mind where Carl is. Carl gets along all right without your help," Ginger said.

"He'll be around looking for you pretty soon," the other boy said. "Shall we tell him we seen you?"

"You tell him NOTHING," Ginger said. "You NEVER MIND." But the mention of Carl seemed to make her proud and excited. She gulped her coke, took Byron by the arm and led him out.

"You still afraid of Carl? That's your boyfriend, isn't it?" Byron asked.

"I'm not afraid of anything."

"Have some gum." She peeled the tin foil luxuriously from the stick, put the gum flat in her mouth, tipped it so the front end went up against the roof of her mouth, and quickly bent it double with a fierce thrust of tongue muscles.

"Well?" she said.

"Come on."

"Where?"

"Where we can be alone."

She didn't answer, but she took his hand and shortly he became aware that she was guiding him, or maybe even leading him, and a little later on he understood that they were going to the UB church.

The grass in the churchyard had been newly mowed, and because it was so dry it felt stubbly under their feet as they sneaked around the building. At the back a stairway went down three feet to the basement, and it was to the well of the stairway that she led him. They sat on the third step.

"Let me throw my gum away," she said. She did not actually discard it, though, but wrapped it in its tin foil and put it in her dress pocket. "O.K.," she said.

So that part of it had not worked out exactly as he had seen it in imagination, and he began to feel, even as she relaxed toward him, victimized and angry. Even the rising, answering, budding thunder of his body that began readily enough had something mechanical and hateful about it. When he put his hand on her breast, he felt both an elation and that he was being cheated. Why was it such a mean slut who was offering him something so nice?

The first time he pulled at her skirt she fought him off.

"These steps would hurt my back," she whispered. "Why didn't you get the car?"

"Let's go up in the grass."

"I will not. What do you think I am?"

She rolled against him, her body within the dress straining against the angles made by his upraised knees. This time he got under the skirt and surprisingly found her hand following his, restraining sometimes, often seeming to guide, controlling him powerfully, but not fighting him away.

Now the action, and even his consciousness itself, limited as that was, centered in the caprice of the two hands under her skirt, the drama moving with a certain order of attempt, resistance, yielding. He withdrew his hand a minute. "No," her breath roared through the whisper. "Don't stop now you fool!" She dragged his hand back.

She gasped and lay beautifully still. Her face left his and turned to the stars, the beautiful, beautiful stars, so far away.

She said—talking aloud now, not whispering, as though whispering were no longer necessary—"We aren't going to keep God out of this union, are we?"

"It's not a union," he said in a pitiful, angry whisper.

He didn't know why it was time to give up, but he did so, lighting a cigarette while something inside prompted him to say in spite of shame, "I need you."

"Ginger," he whispered.

"That's enough now," she said. She was not speaking coldly. There was even a kind of fond chiding in her tone. It was the remonstrance of the completed and all-knowing female to a foolish child. His humiliation was complete.

He imagined for a second that the stair well was surrounded by antagonistic figures—her boyfriend Carl, the woman who had watched with hawk eyes while Ginger worked him up in the church, his mother. Ginger could have saved him from their scorn.

"Let me have it, Ginger," he said in an artificially bass voice.

She slapped at him playfully, not actually touching his face. While her arm was uplifted he caught it. The cigarette dropped from his mouth. He slammed her against the concrete stair well.

"No rough stuff," she said commandingly, but she was down and he had his knee on her belly, ripping the clothes from around her neck. He saw the coal of his cigarette lying on the step and pushed her bare arm onto it. She was fighting back hard, but even when her arm snuffed the coal she didn't cry out.

She hit him in the throat with her fist, so hard he thought something was broken. His head was ringing. Then he struck back with his fist. He hit her right temple and she lay still.

He stood up panting and loosening his belt. Then all at once the air was coming easier, easy and big, into his lungs. Before he could censor the thought it came clearly—*I whipped her.* He let go his belt buckle.

Ginger stirred and crawled toward his feet so that he could stoop almost without shifting his weight and grab the scant silk from around her thighs—the garment catching once on the heel of her shoe, then hanging weightless in his hands. He ripped it across twice and dropped the pieces on her. "Forget me not," he said.

"You hurt me."

"Get home," he said. "Git."

"I'll tell," she said.

He laughed at her. He knew that he could kill her now, but happily he didn't have to. *I whipped her. In a fair fight.* The evil figure she had been, menacing him in his dream, wasn't even there to be thought of now. He had killed that, not just as he'd expected to, but killed it.

"You hurt me. I'll tell. I'll tell your mother."

By God, you got nothing if you waited for what they seemed to promise you. He lifted his foot and gently shoved her away. *Women,* he thought in his restored innocence, and hazily identified them with all the double-cross promises of the world, *they don't even put up a good fight when it comes right down to it.*

He slapped his fist into his palm resoundingly and walked up the steps to the grass. He felt clean as a whistle, free, ready to go wherever he had to.

DOCUMENT I

PETER WEISS

translated by Georgette R. Schuler

Only those who have been here from the beginning can stand life in this town. Even poverty and pain can be endured—if only one has grown up here!

The sun is rising to the zenith. The stars are revolving in their regular orbits, and, deep down in the city, there is confusion and aimlessness. The fault must be hidden somewhere. Where is the root of these distortions? How is it possible that they can all live here—do they do it merely out of habit, without asking? I am living too! I jump up, I slap my body; my skin under the cloth is warm from the blow. I dig my nails into the palm of one hand; there are jagged white marks. Whenever I want to, I can prove my existence to him who stands next to me, by shrieking. But I have to admit that I and my hunger are as good as nonexistent. Not before this hunger expresses itself in action will people begin to be aware of me. How could I make myself understood—I who have come here as an outlaw? I do not know any of the trades they have here. And yet, I have a peculiar acuity of vision. I know this town, I know its challenge. It is as if, when still far away, I had already absorbed and realized everything.

I came here as the one I am, and that is what I wish to appear. I want the impossible: I want to sing and dance here. I begin to sing in a voice hollowed out by hunger, and I dance with movements shaky with hunger. I am wide-awake. I know what impression I am making, but I still do it—because there is nothing else I can do. I dance right in front of the round, bird-seed plank; the birds flutter up in droves, their wings creak and squeak. I dance my pantomime, my voice is drumming the rhythm; I am dancing, tense, ready to flee. Spectators have gathered. A little girl grasps the hem of her skirt and dances with me. If I had had a platform, maybe people would have tolerated me. However, as I am on the ground, on the same level as anybody else, they feel worried, even threatened; a woman pulls back her child, it begins to cry, disappointed because the spectacle is abruptly at an end; there are shrieks and invectives, people are coming nearer, but cautiously, as if approaching a runaway, wild animal. But I am gone before they can catch me. In the next street, I begin dancing again. I begin dancing again, because this is all I can do, because dancing has started within me. And again, quickly, spectators are gathering around me. This time, it is more dangerous. Retreat is blocked by a house wall; right and left, a tightly-packed mass of living bodies with seeing eyes, and before me, incessantly thundering, metal vehicles chained to each other, biting into each other.

I dance right through the crowd and talk to all, and all talk to me. Everything is asking questions: every man, every animal, every cart, every stone. My dancing is my answer. It is the only possible answer I can think of, I can no longer talk in any other way than with the play of my fingers, with the hymn of my disguised voice, with the language that comes, as it were, from a strange star.

It is as if I gave the town a conscience, a soul. And yet, I am just a vagabond who sneaked into it, in the dark, seen by nobody.

In an enchantment that is lifelong—or two steps long, maybe—I dance into the stream of bodies. I feel the acrid taste of their woolen coats between my teeth, on my tongue there is the saltiness of dogs' fur, when they have come out of the sea water. I kiss eyes, ears, throats, shopping bags, hat pins. I dance the give and take, credit and debit. I dance the creditors' attack: how they cling to you, jump around you, lock you into their arms and legs, how they clench their fists in front of you, and threaten you, and growl. I dance of how they know all about you, take down in their books each of your words and actions, and tuck these notes securely away, so they can use them against you. I dance the questions' dance: how questions are consuming you with their unsolved problem of guilt: Why have you not shown yourself? Why have you not cooled my forehead? Why have you gone so early? Why have you not given me what I asked for? I dance the heavy, dark eyes of unfulfilled promises. I dance install-ment pay offs. I dance how you defend yourself, how you shake off importunate creditors, how you allow yourself to be drawn into a conversation with somebody whose black-mail you can no longer avoid; how you cry with exhaustion in the arms of a woman who, really, had come to you to get back a brooch she had forgotten in your rooms.

I dance among the prostitutes in the great town brothel. I dance how they have all sold themselves to each other, how deeply they are in each other's debt, how they all the time exhort each other to pay. Every one has a claim, and every one wishes to have more claims than debts, that is what keeps them alive; among the enslaved, there reigns an imperious, high tension. I dance how the serf goes around in the livery of the potentate, sells one of his hands, buys two back (at a discount, one as a spare), now somersaults at somebody's command, now has a weaker man dancing to the tune of his flute; the weaker man vanishes, murmuring abjectly, bowing reverently, and, in his turn, finds a lisping hunchback whom he can beat with his little bamboo cane. I dance how, every-where, there is but one question: What can I do for you?

Eyes are blinking, hats are swiftly taken off, ears vibrating, chins wagging; everywhere there is an underlying question: and what do I get in return?

I dance a song to the unknown woman who emerges suddenly, whose voice can not be perceived, her whom I can never reach; for it is always too late. She is standing with me at the railing of a ship; her clothes are fluttering in the breeze, the coast can be seen; but it is too late for me to speak to her now. I have been silent too long. It is too late, the train is moving, it is too late to return, to go back the long way, it is too late, the beach is empty, the house is empty. I should have followed her into it, now it is too late; I do not know through which door she has vanished. I dance her whom I keep always losing.

I dance how no one can be without the other, how all ask each other for a word, a single word, I call: eye of a needle, shoelace, evening walk, vase with flowers! Many call: you! I call back: you I you! I dance the great lack from which we all suffer.

I dance by the vendors who are standing behind their counters like heroic defenders of lost positions. Their faces look as if they were about to tear, the corners of their mouths are twitching with the price of their merchandise. But they are holding out! They are holding out! What are you talking about? What do you mean? What do you want with these electrical rabbits, these sculptured cooking pans, these regulations for the hanging of brushes?

I dance that I am hungry and need help; but before I have time to hold out a hand, danger is closing in on me, there are sabers, helmets, whistles, excited shouts; I break through the noose in a zigzag leap, and rush into the streaming torrent of steel and glass.

Here you have me, take me if you can. I am nothing but eye and ear! I tear through arms that stretch out after me, hop across legs that block my way. Flashing cups are tilted out of houses above me, gigantic toothbrushes hack down on my neck. Above each other, beside each other, the same faces are staring, these blue eyes eyes eyes, this twirled moustache,

tache, tache, bubbly, flooded by glue, its small red cheeks puffed-up. One would like to bite into them! Look! Orders filled! Bang! A bicycle tire is punctured. Somebody is swearing, standing near it, somebody in a checkered vest. Do take a message, an apple, a fountain pen, immediately! Don't be silly, come with us! Come with us, rely upon us, entirely! We give you prompt, reliable and confidential service, prompt, reliable and confidential, from the cradle to the grave, prompt, reliable and confidential. Reasonable. You can not hold me; even if you should want to, I am quicker! I have broken all speed records! You cannot hold me, I am encircling you in more than life-size distinctness, all but blinding you! Warning, fresh paint on the floor, don't walk on it! Come with us, we are starting, starting; have your name engraved in china, or better, have your old family portraits fixed up, we are starting! All aboard, there is plenty of room! We are starting! Round trips, round flights, carousels, tops, coffee mills, last day today, today is still time! Come with us, we are starting! We are starting, a drama of unheard-of dimensions is going on, listen to the great dialogue of jealousy, spoken by our old charwoman! Bathroombed for $——— —no, no— certainly, yes, certainly!—It was set on fire! Listen to the star in her passionate love scene, embarrassed teenager that she is! She gushes: "One must measure it carefully, count it all, all, be careful, one can never be sure!"—Have you heard: the girl has been raped, for the ship has been launched, tickets were sold out, because he turned on the gas, the minister wrote on the paper, because the train was late, he won the jackpot, for he had long felt threatened by his neighbor! Oh, the terrible nooses for the spark of thought! Where are we going? Where?

Ragged porters are dragging a crude cross, a bulgy buddha is sitting on it, a house on his head; masses of prisoners have escaped and spread over the streets. The ships are ours! The vehicles are ours! Freedom is ours! We are going to celebrate, and everybody may be with us!

I am present at my own conception, I see a man and a woman on a creaking bed in a basement; a shot is cracking outside, a blood-flooded face looks through the window, groaning: I am hit! I see something of myself in the dark nomad who is sitting near the fire in the steppe; his horse is feeding under the tree, a child is whining in the tent, women are quarrelling.

Deep inside, a beast is shrieking in a metallic voice; black, steel-like shoulders are brushing me; I race over a smooth plain with skates and iceboats.

A tomato is trundling on the ground; a woman chases it, stoops, holds out grasping fingers. A coin is rolling forward eagerly, mocking the man who lost it. I pick it up, it lies in the palm of my hand like a tiny animal. I leap aboard the tall ferryboat that is gliding by. For a few seconds, I find myself suspended above the hardened arena; I feel like an acrobat on a trapeze; then, I push my way through the passenger-crowd on the rocking gangway. I am hanging in a living grape cluster: eyes surrounding me, cheeks rubbing against me, hot breathing on my ear. Soft hips are pressing into mine, cushions shoot into the bend of my knees, I do not bend my knees, I cannot bend my knees; it would be impossible, the bodies all around me keep me upright. A broad leather back is a shield for my chest; an old woman near me is bowing her grey head, her scalp is gleaming through her sparse hair, her flabby breasts have come to rest on my elbow, I can feel her heartbeat. A young man is sporting a tie, he wears it like a flag. What are you fighting for? The question is not understood. Flashing, the flag is hanging down; mud is rising all around it. An archer is raising his weapon above the shoulders of the people around him, he takes aim, jammed in among their heads, he sends his arrow towards a far-away bird. The bird wags its red and gold feathers; wounds gash through its eyes and beak. The quiver is unsatiable, but this bird has a thousand lives; pierced by arrows it escapes from the hunter.

Pennies clatter through the conductor's rounded, metallic hand. It is of iron. Small paper bills are distributed by the grey hand, white grain is snowing down, cut out of paper. A child crouches down among all the legs, picks up the small grain; big shoes tramp on its legs, smashing its fingers. Big shoes tramp on its shoulders, break its collarbone; big shoes tramp on its chest, smashing the frail, pale cathedral of the ribs. There are its jawbone and some small, sound teeth on the ground. I wriggle free from the body-crowd. Through the clothes, the warmth of the blood is penetrating. Wrapped in various coverings, blossoming plants are standing upright; their flower-cup faces rocking to and fro, following the movements of the ferry. Where are they bound for? Who is the owner of the garden? Is he hidden away in the puzzle of these assembled plants? Is he lying on his side, or hanging head downward? Could he be found by turning the picture about long enough? "Is it you?" I ask of all those who are lying on their sides or standing on their heads. Nobody answers. Many eyes have hidden behind thin membranes; they are in a room with all the curtains drawn.

I am fascinated by wrinkles and tiny shades of complexion, hair waves, blouse collars, lip movements. I am fascinated by muscle vibrations, telltale underneath pink or bluish skin; everything happens under this skin, every one is sitting in his tent and blowing from the inside; every one is knotted into his sack and giving knock signals from within.

I push forward, stark naked. But my nakedness is unobserved, people are standing in too dense a crowd, the cloth of their garments is rubbing me, handbags, umbrellas, portfolios are scratching me, elbows are poking into my ribs. "Anybody else with no clothes on?" cries the conductor. "Anybody else who has not redeemed his clothes?" I am being pushed towards the door, thrust out like something superfluous; new life is crowding in from behind; I hop out, fleeing. I still see a small, mirrored face, the face of the driver, heavy, attentive features, grave eyes that have been given responsibility in tumultuous waters. I am off. Where are these frail blossoms headed for?

I have sentenced myself to this town. I have entered this town like an illness, longed-for, because it was felt to be unavoidable. It is there now, and that is fine. Once in it, you need fear no longer. You just let yourself be burned to pieces by the fever.

Once you are here, the best you can do is to give yourself up to it entirely, to resist no more, to refuse nothing. Its sudden gusts of music must exhaust their fury. It cannot be helped. All you can do is to let it flood you, let the piercing noises go down into the deepest cellars. Above all: patience, patience! It will pass. And, besides, these things mean well. Are these sounds not agreeable, and do they not make you feel pleasantly dizzy? They have no purpose but that of nipping doubt in the bud. In the interest of the general blunting of our minds, this spectacle is of outstanding value, like all those pictures projected on house walls—they are merely meant to keep us in good spirits. Everything here serves the best interest of the community. New devices to make things easy and pleasant are being invented every day. We have lots of ideas when called upon to protect ourselves against the grim teeth of the cogwheel that stands for the basic defect underlying everything. And when enjoying such life-protection to the full, we like to hear loudspeakers blare everywhere: "Everything is in order; everything is in perfect order; everything is O.K.!"

There is nothing here that we could change. I alone can save myself. And the only salvation is the wound-fever of wideawakeness.

I can see some who go in search of themselves with the grave-robber's or the poacher's furtive look. Many look for themselves in the fat cross-word-puzzle magazines which you buy at street corners; others devote themselves to curious occupations as soon as they doff their working clothes. They install complicated lighting systems in their rooms to show off to their friends in the evening. Others finger their snapshot collections or rig up small, eager contraptions according to directions and build unseaworthy boats in their backyards.

Everywhere I touch upon man's destinies. Flashes: fragments of conversation, reflections of faces. I see a woman dragging a restive child. It wants to go to the other children playing in the sand heap, but it has to go with her. Go it shall, and nicely. I see a young vendor looking forlorn among icy, metal cases, looking out of their nickeled frostiness. I see a man high up on a pole, working away with strong pliers. I see a handsome, regular face; a half-open mouth indulging in an intensely satisfying cigarette, a light streak of blue smoke. Somebody collapses right here, lying terribly in the way in the gutter, his legs kicking like wheels in a sawmill, darting up into the sky as suddenly as if they were about to have to support it. Froth is bubbling from his mouth, his eyes are wide open, blood is dripping from a skull wound, dripping on a girl's nylons. He is lying there in a humiliating position, among strangers, a well-groomed gentleman with a briefcase jammed under his arm, his shoes highly polished, his tie knotted with care, a clean hanky in his breast pocket.

I kneel down on the sidewalk and drag him up, open his collar, ease his tense fingers. I look down into his white, astounded face. His eyes are staring at me. Somewhere in myself there is a terrible pity, but nevertheless I am frozen into a sharp, cool curiosity. His glance locks itself into mine, asking for mercy, and I cannot do a thing. Far away in the distance I can hear the ambulance siren. It is approaching, hurrying, its scream is becoming high-pitched and breaks forth in victory. Stretcher-bearers lift the man, carry him away without a word, without so much as an unnecessary movement, as if this was the moment they had long been waiting for. I go on, making my way slowly through the crowd, while people are still standing around, eyeing the pool of blood, until a big black dog comes and licks it up. The white of his eyes is gleaming.

Where shall I go? Where shall I go in this merciless glare? The sun-axe is rising to scaffold height. Everything is bound to spiral, on and on, in infinite succession. Everything is bound to shift and change again. I could paint pictures on the sidewalk pavement and strangers' feet would carry them off; I could say words, and people would listen to me or turn away;

I could go in whatever direction I chose; I could lie down and people would lift me and put me to bed somewhere and afterwards put me back where I had been like a vase.

Where shall I turn in this immense mass of life? One has to restrict oneself to a minimum here. What would happen if one broke out of this existence taking out just a little bit above this given minimum of possibilities? Nothing would be enough any more—no house, no vehicle, no street, no jewel, no signal. One bit only! One would then sing in an entirely new way, one would dance, one would throw away whatever one was holding. One would pronounce new words, one would become aware of the fact that hitherto one had never really spoken to another, had never expressed a single thought or feeling; one would expand one's chest and breathe freely; a new light would sparkle in every eye. But everything is rushing forth in a dull rush, so compactly, so gigantically, that even the most enormous efforts are made in vain.

Where shall I go? Where shall I go in the nausea of this noon? I can only wade deeper and deeper into this test of my strength and perseverance, into this consuming, metamorphosing ordeal, until I may finally give myself up to the depth of the ocean that is waiting.

There is still so much life in me. Sprawling on my little leaf afloat on the water, my skin gnawed by sun and salt, my tongue swollen, my eyes half-blind, I still can see the city come toward me with its radiation of apocalypse, and find a foothold on the swaying ground; the raft carries it.

A policeman's eyes are upon me. His golden buttons are shining, the handle of a bayonet is sticking out of his coat. Slender and tall, he comes near me with springy steps, in black elegance. He sees that I do not belong. He takes off his white glove nonchalantly, and spreads his sinewy fingers.

—What are you doing here, what kind of a person are you? he asks, with repressed energy.

—I am a nobody. I haven't got a name. I am a kind of seismograph.

—I beg your pardon. What is your business here?

—I wonder what all this is for. The high walls over there for instance—residences. Can you make out how much truth there is in my words, sir? Is it true that you have only to push a button in there to stand before an altar decorated with statues? Candles are lit, you hold them and find yourself walking through vaults. There is also a game they play around here; it is called thumping. You have to answer the most surprising questions, have to stand all cross-fires; you get excited and talk and talk to prevent them from getting the better of you, but you can't get away from them. All the time, the questioners are scuttling around you; you can't get away. Maybe the whole thing is quite different, after all. What is going on here?

—Where do you live?

—Where should I live? I wish I knew! Is there any place for such as me?

—If you do not answer in an orderly fashion, I will have to arrest you. You act very strange. Have you a job? Can you identify yourself?

—I am working nonstop. Day and night. But the results are only a few crystals in a mountain of dross. My work consists in a sort of conversation: in an anonymous way, we exchange our experiences.

—Who is we?

—We nameless ones. We write little notes, and throw them away for people to find. At twilight, we trumpet softly in the back yards, and those who want open their windows a little.

—Spying, eh? Will you please tell me what you are aiming at?

—Aiming? I am not aiming at anything. I do not have the slightest possibility, not even the wish to attain anything.

—Show me your papers! Have you a right to be here?

—I wish I knew! But why not, if you are here? I don't have any papers. For whom should they be made out? I do not even know who I am.

—I shall take the matter in hand. This case has to be examined. Follow me!

However, I do not follow this activated principle of the law. My instinct for flight bears me off, in one oblique leap like that of an antelope. Since I do not own anything but myself, I have nothing else at stake. I do not shun uncertainty in order to avoid the certainty of a prison. There is no justice for me but that which I choose myself.

And here, in this black, shining car—did they open the door for me, did arms help me in?

I am in the middle of something hard and stiff and soft and polished, something that is humming faintly. I make myself look like a mourner. Slender, pale, with eyebrows furrowed in grief. I push toward the veils. The larger the following, the greater the honor for the dead. I am mourning with you, take me along!

But out of the silence there come glances, out of the shadow of the high, well-brushed top hats, out of the breathing gauze. I can guess at the bodies under their black cocoons. Some of the figures open their garments a little, a white armor is shining, well-rounded over a chest. They are dark knights, these men, their dark hair is clinging to their temples. The skin of their faces is oiled as if for a tournament. They are too dignified to talk to me, but they would like to drive me away with their eyes. Suddenly, a window has been pushed down; as they are lifting me toward it, a hand is touching me softly, a reminder: I feel a spark within me as if it had touched my heart. "Let him stay," says a voice, and I know that I have heard this voice before. The gleam in the woman's eyes behind her veil is singeing me. Her face cannot be seen, only a wisp of hair is showing, black, glowing, not mourning.

There is a long struggle between the voice that lies in the air like the sound of a string, and the hard, armored eyes. The eyes win. The car stops. The door opens in front of the cemetery door. The carriage step gives way under my foot. The asphalt hits my soles. The car drives right through the portal; behind the walls, there is the rustle of trees, there is the smell of wreaths. Somebody cries: "Did they think you **did not** mourn enough?"

Men are leaning against the doorplates, waiting. They are sitting on the ground, with sprawling legs, or pressing against the walls, hands high up as if they had been hung. And they ask, pointing their fingers at me: "Did those fellows want to keep their grief to themselves? Did you not get anything, not even a nickel? Other people make good money that way. Have you got a butt?"

I turn my empty pockets inside out, once, twice.

They wag their hands in contempt, someone makes a bored, croaking sound, another emits a coughing laugh.

I sit down among them, waiting for the veiled woman to reappear. Again, around us, a vision is soaring, is blown away, and re-emerging: a vision of wishes and expectations; we are spinning it, upon empty reels, while near us, workmen are covering an open part of the road with cobblestones, they are pressing and twirling the blue-veined stones into the sand, and letting their hammers fall down on them with high-pitched sounds, others are putting small trees with young leaves into the holes that have been dug near the curb. Inside the park, a bell is beginning to ring. The wind comes, bringing fragments of a litany. Earth is thrown above the roots of the planted trees, heavy muddy boots tramp it down, and the ground is smoothed with spades. A big steam-roller is set in motion; a man in faded-gray overalls, working a long time among the wheels, finally makes the machine hum; black smoke is puffing out of the chimney, the large rollers are moving, slowly; after many maneuvers, back and forth, and aside, they creak over a layer of new stones. The stones are wedged evenly into each other, and the workmen rest on their spades, their arms on the spade handles, one foot on the edge of the metal, their grimy hands folded.

The black figures are coming back along the cemetery avenue. They are walking in a big cluster, closely together, the sun is dancing through the leaves and playing upon them as if with little golden balls. She is there: I know her by her gait. She is holding a white flower against her breast. Her skirt and veil are fluttering in the wind, she is gliding along. Like a sea, like a night, passing the purple-green walls of a bush.

They are going home on foot; no cars are waiting for them.

I am standing near them at the edge of the steel rails, under the gallows of the station; I am standing right near her, but she turns away, she does not take any notice. The whole group is ruled by a matron who is carrying her belly like a slope; the dark men support her, holding her by the arms and hips. They call her Mother, caress her, tap her on the shoulder; one after another, they take her hand and give it to each other, sharing it among them; even I become entangled in the movements of their arms, I say: "Mother," and take the hand. I feel the tear-moist cloth of her gloves between my fingers. But that is wrong, everything is wrong. I do not belong here; two black backs slide together before me like the wings of a folding door, sharply pointed cuirasses are bared at my side. However, the trolley car is already advancing, emitting shrill sounds, it stops with a jerk, its advertising panels rattle against the windowpanes inside.

If only the woman for whose sake I am standing here would give me one look, if only she would show that she knows about me! But she boards the car with the others, without looking at me. She climbs in lightly, still holding the flower against her breast. I call: "Look at me!" But the door closes behind her, wheezing contemptuously, dull-black and shiny-black are moving for a second behind the windows, then, the car hisses off, in a sparking hurry, its conducting wires are swinging to and fro, howling.

The men near the wall have followed the march of events absently. Now they are commiserating. "Did you not get anything for it?" says one, and another: "You must be more submissive—or else be firm and show your weapon at once." A third says nothing. Grinning, he pushes his index finger through a hole he is making with the fist of his other hand, and shoves the finger in and out. Laughter: "That's what you wanted?"

THE OTHER ALEXANDER

MARGARITA LYBERAKI

translated by Kay Cicellis

Editors' Note: The following is an excerpt from a novel called
The Other Alexander *which was published in Greek in Athens
in 1950 and as translated into French by Gallimard last year.
It deals with a double family. Alexander has two sisters
named Aglaía, two brothers named Phocíon, two brothers
named Grigóri and one brother named Alexander like himself.
This is the "Other Alexander" of the title, whom he has never
met but toward whom he feels drawn. The strange situation
is due to a whim of their father, a wealthy mine owner, who
has given his illegitimate children the same Christian names
he has given his legitimate children. As diagramed on the
cover of the Gallimard edition, here is the family plan:*

THE FATHER

LEGITIMATE CHILDREN	ILLEGITIMATE CHILDREN
Aglaía (*in love with Alexander's friend*)	Aglaía (*pregnant in this part of the story*)
Phocíon (*married to Dorothea*)	Phocíon (*the foreman*)
Grigóri	Grigóri (*the tavern owner*)
Alexander	The Other Alexander

247

The Gallimard cover further states:

"*The relationships between the half brothers and half sisters follow the ways of love and hatred. With subtle and poetic skill Margarita Lyberaki tells how they love and destroy each other. Should one look for a symbol in this unusual theme, in this family that reflects itself as if in a distorting mirror? Should one not see in* The Other Alexander *one and the same family, one and the same person—man himself, torn between self-love and self-destruction?*"

"A fine day to get drowned in the ocean," Dorothéa had told me meaningfully as Grigóri pulled the foreman by the hand. The dance was about to begin. And after having scoffed at Phocíon for complaining to his father that Grigóri had a bad influence on the foreman, she added that she had a yearning for Benedictine and traveling abroad again. I took her hand —she thought this was a sign of surrender.

"So you've been abroad already?" I stared at her rough palm insistently

"I simply long for Benedictine," she repeated, as if giving herself to me.

"Your body is lovely," I whispered, "but your palms are so dry." She got cross then. "And you have such a foolish way of preening yourself in front of the sea."

"Phocíon," she cried to her husband, "I'm going up to my room. This isn't a house; this is a madhouse," she added turning to Aglaía, who had gone back to her music. "What was the foreman doing here at coffee time? And why did Father give him Phocíon's name?"

"It's the other way round," said Aglaía. "He gave Phocíon the foreman's name. The foreman is the elder by two months."

"It comes to the same. Anyway, it's a queer idea, giving his godchildren your names. Phocíon, I'm going up to my room. I've bought a record called *I Had To Meet You*," she said, turning to me again, "and I'm going to put it on now. Would you like to come up and hear it?"

Of course, there was no risk in listening to a record, nor had I any prejudices about her being my brother's wife; but my mind was on the dance and the possible meetings it would bring. Nor it would be wise to listen to the record, because the warmth in Dorothéa's room, the warmth and the music and the drinks, had a way of curling round you till it became hard to break away. It was not that they held any particular, irresistible attraction; but precisely because they were merely pleasant, normal, comfortable, they lulled you to indifference until it seemed absurd to go out on nightly explorations, the search appeared senseless, and you said "why all the fuss, why the worry and struggle since there are armchairs in the world."

"Some other evening," I said. She really grew angry then, and slammed the door behind her as she went out.

I imagined her going up the stairs, her body undulating slightly. She rang the bell, ordered a drink, and then the first strains of *I Had To Meet You* floated down from her room.

The landlady at the inn made first-rate sauces, but it is true she was much too fond of using salt and pepper, and so we never stopped drinking water that night. It really became rather funny in the end—the enormous quantities of water we drank, and the way we had to put on the light all the time. Dorothéa rang the bell again; she wanted more logs for the fire.

The region was surely somewhere by the ocean; I no longer have the slightest doubt about that, and I can't think how I was ever able to confuse the two regions since they are so dissimilar both in climate and landscape. She rang again; she didn't like the Benedictine they brought her; she preferred the brand we had had on Saturday. "Yes, the one with the red label."

"Why don't you go up and listen to the record?" Phocíon asked suddenly. He seemed to have grown restless during the last few minutes. Since that telephone call. He kept changing chairs, and his lighter refused to work; as a rule his lighter was always in order, and always in its proper place. At dinner he had started a conversation with Mother—that was also very rare; he had even asked her whether she had suffered much when she gave birth to him.

"What's wrong, Phocíon?" I asked.

"I'm just asking why you won't go up and listen to the record. It's warmer up there."

I realized I would be doing him a favor if I went. How could I possibly have had any prejudices then? The truth of the matter was that I felt rather sorry I hadn't gone up, especially after I imagined Dorothéa walking up the stairs. After listening to the record, I would have stretched my legs out as far as they could go and put them on the little table by the fireplace. "Your manners are shocking, you're such a spoilt child," Dorothéa would have said, and everything would have been easy and pleasant and warm.

I Had To Meet You: she should have put the record on slower; the rhythm was meant to be slower. I was about to go up and tell her so. But a dog barked. "No, Phocíon, I won't go up to Dorothéa's right now," I said, "I'm going out for a breath of fresh air."

It must have been about time for the dance to begin. And then the long vigil outside Grigóri's tavern, patient as a hunter waiting for a flight of birds, immersed in the marsh up to his knees.

Phocíon had to go up in the end. The top floor of the house had been left to the two couples: Aglaía and her husband, Phocíon and his wife. They shared a common living room and wireless. But the gramophone belonged to Dorothéa; she kept it by her bedside and owned a large collection of records.

"Stop that, it's getting on my nerves," said Phocíon as he entered her room.

"I find it fun," said Dorothéa.

"This is the fifth time I've had to hear the same tune all over again."

"I've just bought it, that's why. If you're bored, go to your own room."

They had slept in separate bedrooms since the fourth month of their marriage, because Dorothéa liked playing patience in the evening and kept the light on late—sometimes until early morning—owing to her insomnia, while Phocíon came back from the mines dead-tired and wanted to get some sleep.

"Your sister seems nervous tonight, too; she pretends she has breathing trouble and pains in the heart. She told her husband about it and went to her room. But the truth is she hates me."

"Aglaía is not like us," said Phocíon. "She likes being alone; she can't bear all this talking and arguing."

"Is that why she never stops gabbling when there are guests at home? Her eyes are full of sparks, and she never lets a dance go by."

"Yes, that is true," said Phocíon. "Sometimes she is silent, and sometimes she talks away like mad."

"And she freezes at the least touch of cold, yet bathes in the sea all winter long; and though it takes her ages to take in what you're telling her, yet there are times when she can read your thoughts like a book. She's the craziest of you all, believe me, and Alexander comes a close second. It seems she couldn't get her breath; her heart was about to burst."

"So she's got this anguish too."

"What did you say?"

"Was that the telephone ringing?"

"But that's nothing compared to what happens when the two of them get together. Before the foreman arrived, Alexander was going on about his travels; but it's all a lie, never believe a word he says. And it's not true Saint-Pierre produces Benedictine; it's made in the village next to it—not a village really, almost a town. That was why Aglaía stopped him, and also because she wanted to show him a passage in the book she was reading—horrid, devilish things, all about alchemists trying to find the seed of dissension hidden in matter, and talking about icy fires and black suns. Then all of a sudden Alexander bent over and whispered to her, 'Father has been making practical experiments at our expense, never caring about the anguish it caused us,' and then . . ."

"Yes," said Phocíon, "Aglaía will get no sleep tonight. She's not pretending; her heart is really about to break. But are you sure that wasn't the telephone ringing?"

"Hand me those cards, I want to play patience. . . . Over there, in the bureau-drawer, on the right."

"I must go," said Phocíon. "It's snowing outside, and it's so warm in here that I'll go to sleep any moment—and that I mustn't do. Because of the mines, of course. Why do you think it odd at such a late hour? Anyway, it's something connected with the mines. I can't explain. Besides you'd be bored."

"Don't go, Phocíon, I won't play patience. We'll have a game together, the two of us."

"No, they're waiting for me," said Phocíon. "But *you* will never get a child into your belly."

"Give me those cards," she cried. Phocíon was already gone.

Then she began thinking of Aglaía's husband, who was moderate in his political beliefs—more a democrat than anything else, and very handsome. He loved Aglaía with a kind of stubbornness and covered her up when she went to sleep in the armchair. Then he would turn his gaze to Dorothéa as if wanting to say, "ask me about the mines now." She even thought of breaking the record, because she was sick of it, and because she wanted to make some noise. Aglaía's husband had a sensitive ear.

"What is it, Dorothéa? Is there anything I can do?"

There he was already, discreetly knocking at the door. "Yes, come and help me pick up the broken pieces. Things keep slipping from my hands lately." He stooped in front of her. "Don't go yet; let's have a drink." She shuffled the pack of cards. "What about a game? Here, in front of the fireplace."

"Aglaía has pains in her heart, perhaps I should . . . but it's so pleasant in here. Give me a drink."

"The Syndicate ball has rather upset the family, don't you think?" said Dorothéa laughing. "All of them look strange tonight, different, except the two of us. Tell me, what are we doing here?" She laughed again. "And when Phocíon and

Grigóri begin wrangling, you'll try to get them together with sensible words and a soft voice—and I with my dancing . . . Why should they all insist on going out in the snow when there's heating in the house?"

"And deep armchairs," added Aglaía's husband.

"Alexander has a word for such nonsense. And he also goads Aglaía on. They read strange books together and talk about black suns."

"Listen, Dorothéa, I didn't want to tell anybody—but a little while ago, when Aglaía couldn't get her breath, she kept saying, 'go and help Aglaía,' and when I asked her what was wrong with her, she said, 'Nothing's wrong with me, go and help Aglaía.'"

"Well, what about a game of cards?"

"Yes, let's. Give me the cards. I'll shuffle them."

How hard it is to breathe and live, thought Aglaía, yet it is good to go out walking in the early morning and to swim in the sea. He had not understood her anguish for the birth-pangs of the other Aglaía. He was playing cards with Dorothéa, while Aglaía was having a child; Aglaía was about to have her child any moment, Phocíon had already received a telephone call saying so; perhaps she was racked with agony this very moment, twisting the iron bars on the bedstead, not knowing what to do with her belly and her widening waist, perhaps she was writhing now, not knowing where to put her arms and feet; there was too much of her, she was too big, even her head was too much; if only she could dash her head against the wall; God what a relief to dash your head against the wall and no longer know you are in pain, even though your face remains locked in a stony mask of pain, a still contraction like an explosion of laughter. He had not proved worthy, yet he used to cover her up with infinite care. What did it matter if he looked at Dorothéa; Dorothéa took an interest in the mines and questioned him and listened to his answers attentively—she, instead, was often absent-minded, what was the use of talking to an absent-minded person—Dorothéa used to say the mines were her great passion; she said this laughing so that her hair, her voice, her bosom were all caught in the same undulation, without that sadness ever leaving her eyes; besides she had always been very good at concealing her dry palms and the roughness of her skin. Her own mistake was that she had never managed to learn how to play cards, she couldn't even tell the face cards from each other. Alexander's friend, however, always turned round to look at her when he had finished playing the last note of the last piece of music. She knew this, and held her eyes ready for that brief moment; later on she evoked it again and again, systematically, in a dogged effort, once, twice, three times, but the moment was dimmed, and there remained only the fear that it should grow utterly dim and disappear altogether—let us keep the moment, let us imprison it, build a tall wall planted with tall bars around it so that it will not disappear, even though it threatens to stifle us to death in its expansion.

The bed on which Aglaía was having her child must be narrow, because in a moment like that, no place is large enough, not even the earth. Her body and the last scream from her lips must have invaded the whole earth by now; there was no longer room for houses or rivers or underground trains, and yet again Aglaía must find there was not enough room; Aglaía was in agony, the earth was narrow, even though the houses had gone and the rivers had gone, the earth was narrow and she was in pain."

"Ace of hearts."

Dorothéa's laugh came through to her.

"It's my game," she was saying, because she had nothing to fear here, neither the ocean nor the hollow air between her hands. Here she could pick up a glass and clasp it, and she could shuffle cards. She shuffled with amazing dexterity.

"Are you always as restless as this?" asked Aglaía's husband. He watched her pacing round the table. "You're dropping your cards. Don't worry, I won't pick them up. I know you're dropping them on purpose, so that you can bend over; and you place the bottle here and the glasses there just as an excuse to move about the room."

"You are clever," answered Dorothéa, and as she stopped laughing, the sadness in her eyes became more apparent.

"Did you doubt that?"

"You know, Phocíon has begun fearing you lately."

"What about?" he said, bending abruptly across the table.

He was nearly touching her. She leaned imperceptibly, only for a moment, then instantly threw her body backward. She laughed. "Oh, about me, you mean?" She was laughing. "No, it's about the mines, of course—he's afraid you might take his place."

"He's afraid of the foreman, too. Besides, so am I."

"That ridiculous man who can't utter a word and only knows how to sing *The Foreman's Nosy Nose?*"

"Down in the mines he has power. He keeps us all in awe."

"But not the old man. He's the only real man among you. You're terrified of him, the whole lot of you, the foreman most of all."

"Dorothéa, stop it, you're making me dizzy."

"How dare you? I like pacing round and round, and I'll do it as much as I like and drop the cards so that I may bend over and pick them up. There!" She threw the cards to the floor and stamped on them, sobbing.

"Hysterics," muttered Aglaía's husband. Then in a louder voice he said, "Dorothéa, you have beautiful legs, especially higher up, where the hips begin. I wish I had a hundred packs of cards to scatter about the room, just for the pleasure of seeing you stamp on them."

"Take this pill. It will make you sleep, and then you'll feel nothing," her husband had told her after he'd finished the first game with Dorothéa.

"Who's winning?" she asked.

"I am, of course. All she knows is how to shuffle the cards."

"I hate her," said Aglaía.

"I adore you," said her husband, and he helped her rest her head on the pillows and covered her up.

"The bed is so narrow," she said.

Because no place is large enough then, not even the earth.

"Everything will be all right after you've taken the pill. Try and rest."

Her body and the last scream from her lips must have invaded the earth by now.

"Take this pill," he insisted.

No room left for the houses or rivers or undergound trains.

"They are the very best pills," he repeated.

"Go and help Aglaía," she cried then and took the box of pills from him and threw it out of the window. "On the contrary, I want to understand; I want to see it all and understand. And not confuse houses with trees. I'm suffering Aglaía's pain, and perhaps tonight I'll get to know her at last. I mustn't let sleep carry me away and dissolve me into thin air—things are slippery enough as they are, every day they slip away unnoticed. We can't be bothered to say this is a house and that is a tree; and we can't tell the taste of sugar from the taste of salt. We go drifting from room to room like draughts of air."

"You are jealous of Dorothéa. I assure you that . . ."

But then you can't say 'this is a house' about half-houses. Because there do exist houses cut in two—the way a watermelon is cut in two, right through the middle—some by bombs, and others by the civil war. And there exist slices of houses, thin slivers of houses, a wall standing alone, precariously supported by the adjacent buildings. She had seen the Fiancée in the street today, quite by chance, she had seen her yellow hair, her full bosom standing out against the empty background of a house cut vertically apart. Because of the clean bisection, you could see, inside the house, the cleft rooms, the water pipes, the nails on the wall, and gilt frame framing nothing. As for the furniture, it had been stolen although it was charred and useless. People would come into the broken house and tear away a floor board occasionally; but that did not matter any more for the roof was missing, and the floor remained exposed to the wind and the rain.

"Yes, I know," she said. "It's only because she takes an interest in the mines." She took his hand and stroked it. "Such a pity."

But there hadn't been time to call out to her. Perhaps she hadn't found the courage. She ran after her, very nearly touched her on the shoulder, and noticed how carefree her neck was and the swing of her hair. Then she stood still and saw the Fiancée vanish in the crowd. But she must call out to her, must speak to her, tell her something, anything— about the broken house for instance, and about that old pail which nobody had thought of stealing and which swung emptily between the second and third floor. The Fiancée would have said yes, it's because the sailors are now throwing it overboard to draw water for the deck. The deck must glow with cleanliness, the whole ship must smell clean; airplanes have a smell of their own too, says Alexander, a special smell that the pilots adore, that they adore even more than women's scent, a smell of their own, unlike the smell of a ship or a car. God, she should have called out to her and spoken to her; this was the fifth time she'd let such an opportunity go by, but next time she saw her she would surely call out to her, for she saw the Fiancée quite often, always by chance, yes, extraordinarily often, every time she went out in the street hoping to meet Alexander's friend she came across the Fiancée instead. She turned a street corner and there was the Fiancée, she crossed to another street, the Fiancée again; the Fiancée at the coffeeshop, the Fiancée at the theater, the Fiancée in the morning, the Fianceé in the afternoon, the Fianceé in the evening, ever fair and carefree. And Alexander's friend would touch her and kiss her, at night he would suddenly grip her by the waist and hold her to him—God, she should have stopped her and said: "please, don't ever see Alexander's friend again." It would not be very difficult; she would begin with: "please," or "if you please," or "I beg of you," and the Fianceé would answer, "but of course," or, "with pleasure, if I meet him again, I shall cross over to the other side of the street."

"I assure you there's nothing to worry about. It's only that she has insomnia and is afraid of being left alone."

"I know that tonight my hatred for Dorothéa will be lessened," said Aglaía.

Why did that sadness never leave Dorothéa's eyes, and why should she make those same vague gestures in her bath as in front of the ocean, those same imaginary patterns, finding no support in the empty air. Why should she take the car out and race along the road and yet find no end to the day, no end even when she woke up at half-past eleven in the morning?

She had suffered much from Dorothéa, from her way of laughing and dancing, taking her husband by the hand just when he was about to cover her up, asking him questions about the mines just when he wanted to speak to her, letting out a sudden, strange cry the very moment he wanted to sit gazing at her silently.

"We drift apart a little more every day," she said. "And I've begun waiting for the postman again, the same postman who brought us the mail on the Alps."

"Listen, I'll have one more game with her. She's afraid of being left alone."

"I can't bear these half-houses," said Aglaía.

"She says she has nightmares even when she's not asleep. Phocíon has left. What's come over them all tonight? The bedrooms are empty. They keep talking about some sort of mission. What is this mission that makes them kill each other?"

"Phocíon wants to have it out with the foreman. There isn't enough room for the two of them in the mines; it's simply a matter of who will get the other one out of the way first. Meanwhile Grigóri wants to prove that he believes in fire. And Alexander keeps calling to the other Alexander, and he grows bitter and walks miles on end, not knowing that perhaps he may be able to find him just by remaining motionless. And I suffer Aglaía's pain. I am Aglaía; I do not want to think anything else, neither the postman, nor the eyes of Dorothéa, nor the Fianceé whom I had not the courage to stop in the street. Alexander's friend can squeeze the Fiancée in his arms as much as he likes, he has already diverted my thoughts from Aglaía quite enough; Aglaía is all I want to think of tonight, nothing else. I can see the whole pattern now, a clear line ever since the day I was born and started playing. There's a limpidity, my God, a clarity in the landscape, if only I could always keep this clarity, my God. And our separation, which began at the time Dorothéa married Phocíon; and you watched her walk up the stairs—our separation growing deeper every day, filling me with horror and anguish, as if my breast were swelling, until I wondered what I would do with myself; there was no room for this hugeness. It was agony, and I said where will I find room? The walls were marching against me, moving a few inches every day, until the ceiling began descending, and suddenly it cracked and crashed and crumbled, and the pressure was such that I was freed; I threw the broken glass out of the window—yes, I can see it now, the separation is consummated. I won't let you cover me up again, I won't . . ."

She sat up, looked round the room.

"Where are you?" she cried.

He must have been in a hurry to start the second game. She heard laughter in the next room. A mouse emerged from a hole and began gnawing wood.

"So I was talking to myself," said Aglaía. "I am afraid."

Another mouse appeared. Now they dashed back and forth across the floor. One of the water pipes must have split open; or perhaps the mice had crept up from the mines.

"I am afraid," she said.

They ran back and forth, more mice—hundreds of mice. They had come up from the mines.

"I am afraid," she screamed.

She hid her head under the bedclothes, brought her hair

over her face. It was a kind of protection. "Some day I've got to get away from this place," she said. "It's years since I last swam in the open sea. *With a View of the Sea*, wrote Grigóri over the entrance of his tavern, and that too is a lie. I am afraid. And Alexander's friend, who never understood, who never knew how I coaxed the postman into letting me empty his old leather bag, he never suspected what a second meant in the run of a long day and a long night—what all the seconds of waiting meant. My sister Aglaía is having a child. Such clarity, my God, such supreme clarity. The separation is consummated; I've got to tell you, I won't put it off for a moment. I shall rise and walk among the mice, now, barefoot, I shall walk over the mice to you and tell you."

The most difficult part of it was to put her head out of the bedclothes, make the final decision, and gather her hair back into a knot. She looked toward the window; it was snowing. And from the window came a sudden felicity, which pierced her spine, reached her heart and the tips of her fingers. Her hands met and knew each other; it was the coolest refuge for her face, and her feet were warm in spite of the cold in the passage—if at least one did not die, if only one never died —nor did she feel the slightest shudder when she opened the door and saw her husband on the bed with Dorothéa.

"You must excuse me," she said. "I've only come to say that the separation is consummated, that it is snowing, and that I'm not cold or afraid any more."

COMING NEXT WEEK

JACK JONES

Three hundred blue-eyed dogs hunting for homes
Wriggle in to lick the palms of the War College children
But the technocrat nurses scream for the rifles
The dogs escape between their legs, licking at trifles.

The analyst howls and all night the X-rays are wheeling
Through dreamers to doctor the itching germs of stealing.
On the white lake of dream-poison the rowboats overturn
And the barracuda dance through the flesh of their scorners.

The sun prods the dead. "Jesus Aitch!" The warmed sand
Up and slides over gray boards through weeds on demand
Of the Really Last Hope IV. In cities nine inches quickly
Fills the nostrils of the weeping, prone and sickly.
            The goners die in the sunsea lapping on the Gate.

(As well as certain others——) Cops drag the sand all day
Again the nicer fish swim in the canals, scared but gay.
And the cost of living drops below zero. The paper blight
Resprouts in green print and the sun is left on all night.
            Not one of the trotting girls still denies a Strait.

"What more could we ask?" the soapboxes told each other.
"Hooray! Enfin! Viva!" (No more dam soap either.)

THE PRINCESS IN THE PECAN TREE
or *What The Cicadas Say*

E. N. SARGENT

"Rascals!" said the old man in his thin summertime voice. "Rackety rackscallions!"

Buzzin cicadas all over the pecan tree, havin their biggest blow in years. Buzzin and eatin and buzzin. Where devil did a crowd like that appear from? Brandnew shiny buzzers too, bold as brass and twice as noisy. Hold it there, fella, the eyes a Texis are upon you.

Smack went the old man's newspaper. Missed him. Or was that another one already fillin the pew a the departed? Bunch a chawn pokerfaces. Same difference if you hit 'em or not, deck's loaded. What you rather do, Cady, cheat or eat?

The old man left his paper drop and settled back in his rocker for some more time to go by. Takes time longer to travel them long Texis miles.

Late afternoon, with the tar nation streetcars rattlin out east where they didn't use to be no roads much less rattle-tracks. Some things change, some things not. Always nice and cool in the shade a the pecan tree. Big dark pecan leaves hangin down, makin it look like night up in there. Good cool shade for an old man to rock in.

Never could rock in peace though. Always somebody callin from the house, "Poppa, you know I'm busy, can't you keep MaryAnn outa that sun?"

Can't keep a kid outa the sun. Kid loves the sun the way an old man loves the shade. Shade sets like ice in the bones, sun sets a fire in 'em.

MaryAnn's got the summertime blues, nobody to play with and nothing to do with herself. Miss Question Box. She'll stick you with questions like stickerburrs if you don't watch out.

Old man use to lie in the sun himself, he did. Longtime ago. Use to walk out at night too, and look at the moon.

One day wayback he lay so long in the sun talkin or somethin, he took a fever. And that same night he walked out in the yard while he was asleep, still talkin. Sleepwalked right out under the pecan tree. They found him ice cold, holdin onto the trunk with both arms.

Musta been a dream. And the graceful white swan goes glidin on. Long hair she had, that dream. Long and soft and silky. An cool white skin no matter how the sun beat down. An big dark eyes. Now what color was those eyes?

Just like a young sprout, to ride day and night after skin and hair, and leave the eyes get away. Eyes are the real man rustlers. Where did she appear from with those eyes a hers? Wide and dark they were, like the lonesomest places in the night.

Never mind how many wives you married and buried, your best girl's the one you can't have. Held on by a thrill, she did, the only draw left in the game.

"MaryAnn. Maree Ann! Poppa, are you mindin MaryAnn like I said?"

No sign a Annie. She must be off someplace makin up question-answer games to pass the time. Miss Question Buzz, off in the buzzin summer.

Cicadas carryin on like crazy. She'll give 'em a run for their money. What say, Cady?

Old man remembers finding an old Spanish book up in the attic one day. Be a spick if he didn't find that book the same day the fever took him. Had long black lines a poetry goin on and on like the cicadas.

Too much sun the doc said, then too much icy cold that night out under the pecan tree. Which is worse, Doc, the fever or the chills? Left him with a limp, that day and night did.

Ah sweet mystery a life, and how would you say *that* in Espanyol? When you're a young sprout you hold the big juicy cards, and the stake's all there ready for the ante. What they write the songs about.

Better songs in the old days a course, had more meanin. Nowdays they just yell at you til you wish you was deaf and gone.

Where's the words these days? Where's the meanin? Even the cicadas sounded different back there when he was a kid, made kinda sense. There was somethin they use to say.

Somethin . . . and somethin . . .

Mary Ann hides behind grampa's rocker til he begins to snore. Then she creeps away into the sun.

If you lay in the sun on a hot summerday you see rainbows and feel like you're flyin. More fun than when you get to mix a cake.

MaryAnn, MaryAnn.

Let 'em call. Your grampa looks to be miles away, over yonder under the pecan tree. Your bugs in your glass jars, even, are biggern him.

What a big bug in that one! Big bug through the rainbow, when did you get caught? Sun get you mixed up?

Looks to be a cady-bug. Did he mean to go flyin in the sun or did that big old pecan tree get in a pet and shake him outa her hair?

Lookit him there! He's talkin to himself! He's rubbin his legs together in a secret!

Listen, if I promise to let you out, will you promise to tell that secret to me?

Slip, slide and out he comes.

He's gonna fly away without answerin! No sir, down goes that jar on you! You tried to cheat! One more chance is all you get.

This time the cady-bug steps outa the jar like a gentleman and parks on MaryAnn's hand. He's wearin tight green pants and a snappy vest, and his eyes are poppin out like shelled pecans.

He rubs his wings together a couple times, and jerks his head up and down.

"La Prin-cess-a," he says, scrapin like a old door hinge. "La Princessa esta-a trrist-e."

"Speak American, bug! I can't understand Mexican and you know it!"

"Please excuse, Señorita," he says in a perfeck-gentleman voice. "I try, ah so hard to explain. There is in the pecan tree a Princessa."

He means a princess! In the pecan tree! Mary Ann nearly jumps outa her skin.

The world goes round and round til the only thing left is the big dark tree.

"Oh mister bug! Could I—could I see her sometime?" Go for a nice long visit in the pecan tree. Wouldn't people be surprised?

The cady brushes a speck a dust off his vest and starts talkin fast and low like the men who come by sellin things.

"Why not, Senorita? Many days she is triste—sad—because she have no one to play with."

"You mean—she's a little girl? Like me?"

"Well Senorita, she is not large. And she very much enjoy to play with children."

The cadys in the pecan tree go off like an alarm clock, *trrist-e*. Then they stop.

"Is it dark in there?" asks Mary Ann.

Here he takes on friendly. "But no! Jewels are all over the walls, which give light like a rainbow."

Mary Ann can't help noticin when he says "jewels" he seems to puff up. How funny he looks, swellin up like a frog.

"Jewels and candies," he says, "each more delicious than the other."

Mary Ann sees herself pickin 'em off the wall like prizes. First the rubies and the ruby-colored candies with the cherry centers, then the lemon drops and the yella stones, all the pretty, pretty things.

"She has toys also. Golden balls from Spain, china dolls from France, puzzles from China, Turkish picture books which are turning their own pages. But her most wonderful treat is the little cakes she bakes. Mmm, deliciosa!"

"What flavor are they?"

The cady-bug aint answerin.

"Don't she let you have any?"

"Errr, I do not rememberr. You see, I do not eat cakes, I eat other things."

Trriste, triste . . .

The cady-bug is looking away in the distance and sniffin the air like he can smell somethin.

"I think at this very moment she is placing the cakes in the oven for her guests."

"Oh." It strikes Mary Ann what a dressy bug he is. "Is the princess havin a party?"

"Si, she give a teaparty today. Was for one person only. But with you, will be for two."

"I wish I was wearin my party dress."

"Ah but there is no need to change the dress. Her favorite color is blue like your apron, the color of the sky."

From the pecan tree, *triste, triste, triste . . .*

"I want to go see the princess! I want to go! I want to eat the cakes and look at the pretty picture books!"

"She will be delighted. I take the liberty to formally invite you, and I accept the R.S.V.P.

Triste!

"So what for we wait? Can you curtsey, Señorita? Here—" and he takes Mary Ann by the hand.

His hand feels spiny like a bunch a twigs. A funny feelin comes up in her about curtseyin to somebody she aint met, like she was to make a promise without knowin what.

"It is nothing," says the cady-bug. "Regard me!"

He twirls, and bends all his legs at once. "You see?"

He looks so aggravated with all his knees stickin out that Mary Ann's got to laugh.

"Not for laughing matter," he says good and sharp. "I, Señor Cicada de Nada, who eat everything and know everything, take the responsibility to escort you. Do not release my hand please."

Mary Ann looks at the pecan tree so deep and green, so far away.

"Will grampa try and stop me?"

"He cannot. He do not see you. He thinks you play games."

Before she knows it he's hurtin her arm with his handgrip, tryin to force her. "Curtsey Señorita, so our travel can begin."

"Wait a minute, please Mr. Bug. Let go my hand for a minute!"

The cady-bug has to obey but he sure don't like it. He looks maddern a hornet.

She's ready to cry, for being afraid he won't take her to the princess now. But she's burnin up with questions.

"Why do I have to do that curtsey before we even start?"

"What makes you change on me from friendly to hurtin mean?"

"How come you got so big while you was talkin?"

He don't answer. He is studyin the clouds.

"And why do you keep callin me Señorita all the time, even when you're mad? There's somethin funny about you, Mr. Bug. You holdin a grudge from bein kept in the jar?"

The cady whirs, his softest whir of all.

"At your pleasure pretty lady, and your mercy. I do not change, I am always polite. My name, for example, is called Mr. Cicada, not Bug. Bug is not nice." He stares right into her with his shiny eyes.

"Cicada," says Mary Ann. "Mr. Cicada."

Then she gets up slowly, and slowly she places her hand in his. Careful and slow like a sunflower she moves her head.

Triste says the cicada movin his eyes in a circle. And she follows 'em in a slow turn like a dance.

Noddin his head he says *triste,* and she bends in a low curtsey.

Like a closin sunflower she don't bring up her head no more. Even with Cicada rubbin his legs like crazy she don't come up with a single question.

Now they two begin to walk towards the pecan tree. How slow they go! It turns out Mr. Cicada was tellin the truth all the time. He ain't grown bigger after all, it was she done the changin. She MaryAnn, musta shrunk smaller and smaller without knowin.

How tiny and dry she has grown. At the rate they're goin, the cakes will be all gone by the time they reach the palace. A blade a dead grass cuts her face, and she stumbles. She wishes she had wings like the cicada so she could fly.

"It would be more rapid to fly," says he, "but I am not allowed to carry so young a guest so quick."

"Look out for grampa!"

"The old man? He will not wake. Or if he do, he can make no trouble. He has know the little lady one long time, and he admire her very much."

La Princessa esta triste, que tiene La Princessa?

"What I quote you, old man, is a poem. Have you forget the poems you read in youth?"

"None 'a your tar nation business, you buzzin buzzard." Sure is some slicker, sellin satan knows what. "Clear off now, fore I send you to kingdom come."

Cicada don't take fright easy. He knows people can't get enough of a good thing. "Forgive me, but the youth do not fade. Ah, the young man's dream she do not forsake him. Remember La Princessa?"

Rackety-rack he goes like a carny pitch, and does thought readin on the side. Señor Cicada The Great. (How much willya pay me to bury yer payast, yer present, and yer future?) He would know about the girl with the soft white skin. (Step this way, this way inta the tent.) That's what she was though, some kinda gypsy princess. (Howja like a leetle game back there after hours?")

The old man keeps his trap shut. No use askin for it at this stage.

"You have not forget the Little Lady?"

Old man sighs and hitches in his chair. He can't help payin attention to this slickspittle. (Wots the matter son, got a snake in yer britches?) Thy belly is a heap a wheat. And the dance they do is enough to kill a joo. The old man opens up in spite a himself.

"Does she still do that glidin dance?"

"Si, Señor." Cicada puts a shot a oil in his voice. "But she is older now of course, like you."

Old man knows he's bein buttered up for the pot. Probly a no-limit game, at that.

"You fellas are tricky," he says. "Can't tell what the deal is when you start jabberin. I wouldn't be surprised if that little lady left town long ago and there's nothin down inside this here tree but worms." And he gives a rap on the bark.

"Worms, Señor! But no! What give you that idea?" (Come on in, boy, have a look, have a look, see the little princess, Little Andalusia, she walks, she talks, she dances AND she disrobes as far as possible.) "She have wait and wait for you, all these years!"

Now the old man gets to feelin ashamed, and that's a feelin he aint had for a long time. Pore little Andalusia, he sure hates to think a her bein stood up!

"Does she take it hard?" he asks.

Cady gives a sound like a snicker. "Take it?" he says. "Si, she take it. Hard, soft and medium, for sure she take them all."

"You're not the same greaser use to get me worked up as a kid, are you? Use to come round with tales a white soft skin and all that? Why, she wouldn't be able to hold up her head if she knew the things you use to say about her!"

"Was for sure one other cicada, Señor. Rest peaceful, that cicada was of course fourteen year locust, he disappear a long time back." Confidential is the word for Cady.

Might's well have the whole story if it's bein buzzed about. Let's have it, Cady, what kind a secrets has she got deep down under them roots? If not worms or blindmoles or creepin night things, what then?

"Musta been plenty other fellers she waited for, not just me," says the old man with his head hangin down and hurtin.

Cady buzzes round that posy without stoppin. "Man to man," he says, "you are no stranger to the little lady. You know the dance she do. Will you not be her partner?" (Who's stayin, boys, who's stayin for the next show?)

The old man don't look up. Seems like it's pretty late to start dancin now.

Cady goes back to his thought readin. "But she do not only dance. *She can also cook.*"

No sign from the old man.

"All men adore her cakes. Because they make a man of the young schoolboy, and they even make strong the most worn-out elderly gentleman."

Cakes! The old man's heard a such things, of course, but never set no store by it. Blood rushes to his head, and his hands start tremblin. By devil, he'll stay in the game if it kills him.

"She wear a blue apron to see through, and a little blouse which fall from her shoulder like a mist. Mmm, preciosa!"

The old man can almost reach out and touch the slippin veil. He can almost feel the magic cakes easin the pain in his chest and givin back his powers.

To hell with gossipin grannies! Bring on the weepin and teeth-gnashin, the old man's stickin by.

"I'm sure sorry to hear she's blue," he says devil-may-care.

"You could cheer her up, Senor. I think you are not so old like you pretend."

By jakes there's life in the old dog yet! A leetle after hours game, eh? Let's see, Cady, how many aces you got, four or five?

Whoa there. Hold on. Wasn't there somethin ought to get done first? Somethin about MaryAnn.

"Can't she come outside for a minute?" (Ask the little lady to step outa the tent.) Tell her yers truly is at her service, but just now I got somethin to attend to."

"Alas Señor, she never do that. Sometimes she seem to come out, but she only *seem*. She would look in you with an eye which have no color, only dark. And she would only send her shadow. You know Señor, the shadow is not so beautiful."

The old man shakes his head kinda weak. The pain's comin back, and with it somethin chilly as a blue norther spreadin in his veins. He gives the kinda smile a couple pairs gives a full house and says, "All right, you catalogue a temptations, you got me cold."

He turns up the palms a his hands to catch a dapple a sunshine that's slipped down into the shade well under the pecan tree.

Sun! That's what it was about MaryAnn. "Just let me fetch MaryAnn outa that sun—"

"Ah but there is no time; you must hurry Señor! You know how to bow? I, Cicada de Nada, who strip all things bare, will show you. Regard!"

Little Andalusia musta gone formal in her old age. Grampa laughs, and that laugh feels good. Nothin like a good laugh to warm the cockles of a heavy loser.

"Not for laughing," horns in Cicada quick and sharp. "Your hand, Señor!"

The old man tries the bow on his own, and don't do too bad with it. He sees himself bowin and handkissin, and then. . . .

Cady grabs ahold a the old man's hand with his spiny claw, and pulls. It's like bein pulled by a bunch a icicles. (And now if you will step this way—)

"Wait a minute, don't rush me. I got to think."

"What you think about anyway? The granddaughter? I tell you she will not see! And if she do, it make no difference. She knows all about the little lady."

"What? MaryAnn?" The old man sinks down in his chair.

This wasn't part a the game. He may never rise up outa this rocker again, but he will put up a last ditch fight for Mary-Ann.

"Where's my newspaper!" He hits out this way and that way all round the rocker. "Nasty, noisy bugs all over the place! I won't have you foolin with MaryAnn, you hear? That Andalusia aint no company for her! You can take your dirty stories someplace else!"

"Be kind to put down the newspaper, Señor. I do not tell her the bad story. I say our little lady is a nice playmate who has pretty toys to play with."

"MaryAnn! Annie! Where are you!" Only him to stand between her and this lyin, cheatin . . .

Got to get up. Never so weak before. Wasted all his strength bowin to a carny queen. Oh Annie.

"No use for call, Señor," says Cicada. And he's the biggest buzzer the old man ever saw.

Trriste!

"Sure God, I won't let you take her! You leave that kid alone! I'll blast you, I'll—"

There's a rumble 'a thunder in the distance, and the cicadas in the pecan tree go silent. Rain. It's goin' to rain.

"Hurry! When the rain falls her stove go out, and the party is spoiled."

Thunder rollin, big drops fallin on the leaves. The dried-up world with its wings and voices still now, for the freshenin' rain.

"MaryAnn! Poppa! It's rainin!"

Mary Ann drops Mr. Cicada's arm and goes runnin towards grampa. Her blue apron flies over the grass like a bird.

Grampa's eyes start open with a tremble. He catches a flash a blue, then two eyes are starin into his, wide dark eyes with the night in 'em.

The old man turns to ice and can't make a move.

"Come on, Grampa, you'll get all wet!"

"Why, it's you MaryAnn."

Not this time. Not yet.

From the house, "Come on in outa that rain! Swear I don't know which a you's the worst!"

"Come on!" Mary Ann pulls grampa's hand. "Come on!"

He finally makes it up outa the rocker, with the help a that warm hand pullin him. A big wet buzzer tumbles down off his collar and lands on the cane seat. "Grampa, there was a—a cicada on you!"

Screenporch only a step away now.

The porch, the house, and the rain on the roof. Praise be.

Mary Ann swings on grampa's hand and jumps the mud-holes. She feels like splashin and cakewalkin under the drain-spout, but somethin holds her by grampa. Somethin buzzin on-an-on like a question.

"Grampa?"

"What."

"What do the cicadas say?"

THE DEATH OF MOHAMMED

TAWFIG AL-HAKIM

translated and with an introduction by William R. Polk

Drama, as a recognized form of Arabic literature is of very recent introduction and cannot be said to have found its place alongside the more traditional and popular "readings" of poetry and stylized rhymed prose. Drama is, indeed, an example of the impact of Western culture on that of the modern Arabs, and like many other aspects of that impact is still only partly digested. Yet Arabic has long had in the "Shadow Play" and the *Karagöz* a sort of folk drama form similar to European Mediaeval puppet shows, and so it is at first sight somewhat surprising to find that Arabic totally lacked a drama form in its written literature, and, that when it came into Arabic, the inspiration was Western, although to a certain extent the lure has been the "local," thriving young monster, "Hollywood on the Nile," the Egyptian film industry.

In recent years a number of attempts have been made to take the Western form, drama, and apply it to the traditional subject matter of Arabic literature. And of the various attempts, the play, *Mohammed* by the Egyptian novelist and shorty-story writer, Tawfig al-Hakim is probably the most engaging. In this play, Mr. Hakim has *written* very little; rather he has extracted the lines said by his characters from the reported speech of his heroes attributed to them in the collections of "Tradition" (*Hadith*) gathered in the centuries after his death on the sayings and doings of the Prophet of Islam and his associates. This has both been a limitation and a source of power. On the one hand, Mr. Hakim has had to glean, from what is fortunately for him a vast literature (there supposedly being some half a million stories, descriptions, and details on Mohammed current at one time in the Middle Ages of which at least ten thousand are known today), his raw material and fit it together like a mosaic. And because of the semi-sacred nature of his material, Mr. Hakim could take few liberties; the words were there and he has tried not to add to them or alter them. Further, because the words were spoken thirteen hundred years ago (this being 1333 A.H.), they are at least as strange to the modern Arab ear as is King James Biblical English to the modern American. However, and it must be admitted that this cannot be translated, every word is steeped in emotional flavour and is evocative of a set of sentiments absorbed in the process of growing up in a Muslim family.

Islam has always been at once a religion, a state, and a code of conduct. The basis of all three is set out in the Bible of Islam, the Koran, which is believed to be the "word" of God as revealed to Mohammed and, which he maintained, is identical to that previously revealed to the Jews in the *Torah* (Mosaic Law), and the Christians in the Bible. The "rules" laid down in the Koran of course reflected the society of Mohammed's own times, and, in changing circumstances, had to be augmented or reinterpreted. Thus recourse was had to the way Mohammed himself, in his own life, went about things. Family traditions, gossip, odd bits and pieces were memorized or written down and evaluated on the basis of their sources. A fairly typical *Hadith* is the following:

"Mohammed ibn Kathir related to me, Sufyan was informed by Mansur who got it from Abu Wail from Abu Musa al-Ashari who heard from the Prophet, God bless and save him! , 'Feed the hungry and visit the sick and set free the captive.'"

The energy with which the life of the Prophet was mined can only be understood as the desperate attempt made by the whole community to produce a new *Sunna* (code of life) to replace the older, tribal codes undermined by Islam. Actions in new situations were thus justified by a sort of "legal fiction" based on some saying, action, or witnessing of the speech or acts of others by Mohammed. Thus, Tradition has become canonized as a source of law and ethics second only to the Word of God, the Koran.

Needless to say, the action and the various characters of the play are at least as well known to an Arab audience as stories of Jesus and the Twelve Apostles would be to an American (or an Arab) audience. This, however, affects the modern Arab playwright differently from what one might suppose: rather than being the delight of the Islamic equivalent of a Sunday school, the play is *ipso facto* beyond the pale. The sacrosanct stature to which Mohammed was raised in the centuries after his death, in direct contradiction to Koranic instructions, make performance of the play impossible. Indeed, a film which, very piously, wished to portray the Prophet was banned by the censors in Egypt supposedly because an actor would have played the part of Mohammed.

It is perhaps because of the problem he has faced on this account as a playwright that Mr. Hakim has suggested the following scene (7 of the final act) for inclusion here. The scene is the death of the Prophet and presents the tremendous emotional stress brought by his death to his young and insecure community. Tradition indicates that in his life, some of his followers had already, despite his constant denial that he was "more than a messenger," ascribed to him superhuman attributes. Some seem to have assumed that he would live until he had converted the world to Islam or that his "death" would only be a cover for his rise to Heaven, as the Koran explains the rise of Jesus. Surprisingly graphic is the portrayal of the bitter dispute over his death; this strife was to be temporarily put aside by the tribal rebellion which followed Mohammed's death. Tribes quelled or diverted, however, this conflict was to break out anew and to remain a constant tension within Islam. Thus, in this scene, we can see the seeds of much of the subsequent history of Islam.

DRAMATIS PERSONAE:

AISHA: *The favorite wife of the Prophet.*

OMAR: *Later to be Second Caliph (successor) to Mohammed.*

ALI: *Son-in-law, cousin, and fourth Caliph of Mohammed.*

ABBAS IBN ABDUL MUTTALIB: *Uncle of Mohammed, a strong enemy now a warm supporter; ancestor of the Abbasid Caliphs of Baghdad.*

ABU BAKR: *Father of Aisha, First Caliph, and Mohammed's most trusted supporter.*

MOHAMMED: *The "Messenger" of God (also called Ahmed)*

FATIMA: *Daughter of Mohammed, Wife of Ali, and ancestor of Fatimid Caliphs of Egypt.*

GABRIEL: *The Angel who delivered the Koran to Mohammed.*

THE ANGEL OF DEATH

BURAIRA: *A woman of the household.*

AL-MUGAIRA: *One of Mohammed's followers.*

(*In the house of Aisha . . . the Prophet is on his death bed, and his women folk are behind a curtain which hides them from his male relatives and companions.*)

OMAR (*enters and whispers to Ali and to Abbas*): The people are asking how the Messenger of God is this morning.

ALI (*whispering*): He has entered upon the morning, thank God, much better.

ABBAS (*looks at the face of the Prophet and whispers*): I swear by God, I recognize death in the face of the Messenger of God, just as I have recognized it in the faces of my brothers.

ABU BAKR (*touches the Prophet*): Oh Messenger of God, truly you are weakened and are suffering very much.

MOHAMMED (*in a weak voice*): Yes. . . . I am suffering as much as two men like you can suffer.

ABU BAKR: You shall have double recompense.

MOHAMMED: Yes, by Him in whose hand is my soul, there is not a Muslim pained by sickness or any other distress who will not be unburdened, as the tree drops its leaves, of his sins by God. (*The sound of yelling and crying is heard from the Mosque, the place of prayer in Mohammed's house.*)

ABU BAKR (*whispering to Ali*): What is this noise in the Mosque?

ALI (*whispering*): I fear that Abbas has gone out to tell the people!

MOHAMMED (*points toward the curtain which separates the Mosque from the living quarters*): Who are those?

ALI: The Companions—the men and the women—are crying for you.

MOHAMMED: What makes them cry?

ALI (*with a low hesitating voice*): They fear that you will die. . . .

MOHAMMED (*feverishly*): Pour on me the contents of seven cups of water from several wells, and bring me an ink pot that I may write for you a testament which will save you from going wrong.

OMAR (*whispering to the men around him*): Pain has overcome the Messenger of God. You have the *Koran*. And the Book of God suffices us.

ABU BAKR: Nay, . . . draw nearer. Let the Messenger of God write for you.

ALI: No, . . . what Omar says is right . . . (*The argument grows more violent among the men.*)

MOHAMMED (*speaking impatiently to them*): Get away from me. . . . Get away from me . . . !

ABU BAKR: We have become heavy on the Prophet in his suffering. . . . Let us go. (*The men leave, and Aisha and the other women emerge from behind the screen.*)

AISHA: Oh Messenger of God . . . you are anxious and vexed. . . . Had any one of us women behaved in such a way you would have been astounded at her.

MOHAMMED (*musing to himself*): Verily pain weighs heavily on the beliver in order that he might be forgiven for his sins.

(*Fatima weeps, not understanding Mohammed's words.*) Don't cry my child . . . but say that we are dedicated to God and to Him we are returning. To every person on earth, there is a compensation for every calamity.

FATIMA: And even you, oh Messenger of God must go through this?

MOHAMMED: Even I.

AISHA (*to Fatima*): He is exhausted from the fever.

MOHAMMED (*starting up slightly in his bed*): Aisha, what did you do with that gold?

AISHA: What gold?

MOHAMMED: The six dinars which I had.

AISHA: I have them.

MOHAMMED: Mohammed will not be worthy of his God if he meets Him with this gold in his possession . . . spend it all on charity. . . . The Prophet must not be inherited.

AISHA: I shall spend them.

MOHAMMED: Please God, let me die poor . . . don't let me die rich; and put me among the miserable. (*He lies down as though to sleep.*) Now I can rest.

AISHA (*putting the head of the Prophet on her breast*): Oh Messenger of God! I beg God for your recovery and for your good health!

MOHAMMED (*fixing his eyes toward the sky—as though soliloquizing*): Nay! Pray for me to meet the most exalting of friends.

AISHA (*silent tears falling from her eyes*): You were given the choice and you have chosen; this I know by the One Who sent you with the Truth.

MOHAMMED (*in a barely audible voice*): A cup of water.

AISHA (*to the women*): Quickly bring me a cup of water. (*They bring a cup.*)

MOHAMMED (*wets his hand and wipes his face*): God help me against the anguish of death!

FATIMA: Oh, how pained you must be Father!

MOHAMMED: Your father has no more pain after this day. . . . Draw near me, oh Gabriel! Draw near, Gabriel. Oh Gabriel, come to me. (*He sees Gabriel, who has come down to him.*)

GABRIEL: Oh Ahmed (*"most praised," another name for Mo-hammed*) God has sent me to you as an honor to you, as a bounty to you, and uniquely to you, asking you about that which He knows better than you. He asks how you feel.

MOHAMMED (*staring intently and speaking from the heart without anything being evident to those who stand around him*): I find myself, oh Gabriel, afflicted and grieved, oh Gabriel.

GABRIEL (*pointing to an angel standing behind him*): Oh Ahmed, this is the Angel of Death who asks permission to enter unto you—and he has never asked permission from any of the sons of Adam before you nor will he ever from those after you.

MOHAMMED: I grant it to him.

THE ANGEL OF DEATH: Oh Messenger of God . . . Oh Ahmed! Verily God has sent me to you and has ordered me to obey you in anything that you bid me to do: if you order me to take your soul, I shall, or if you order me to leave it, I shall.

MOHAMMED: And you will really do what I tell you to, oh Angel of Death?

ANGEL OF DEATH: Yes, because I was ordered to obey what you command.

GABRIEL: Oh Ahmed, verily God longs for you.

MOHAMMED: Go ahead, Angel of Death, and finish the task you were ordered to perform.

GABRIEL: Peace upon you, oh Messenger of God! Today is the last time that I will descend to Earth. (*The two angels rise, leaving Mohammed a still corpse.*)

AISHA (*notices that the Prophet has become heavy on her breast, so she lays him down on the bed and covers his face with his mantel, crying out shrilly*): Come to me! Come to me!

THE WOMEN: What is it? (*seized with anguish and fear*)

AISHA: Oh, my lost one! The Messenger of God has died! The Messenger of God has died! The Messenger of God has died!

FATIMA: Father, . . . Oh, Father!

THE WOMEN: Oh, mourning!

FATIMA (*sees the body and screams out*): Father, . . . Father, . . . Oh Father, whose abode is Paradise. . . . Oh Father, whom we commend to Gabriel. . . . Oh Father, how close to his Lord is he!

AISHA (*weeping and sobbing*): The Messenger of God has *died!* On the pain of my heart; oh, calamity. Now our link to God has been broken away from us!

BURAIRA (*rushes into the room*): Omar and Abbas and some men with them are requesting permission to enter to see the Prophet!

AISHA (*to the women*): Hide yourselves behind the curtain! (*The women hide themselves, weeping the while.*)

OMAR (*enters and hurries up to Mohammed, raising the cover from Mohammed's face*): Oh, . . . he has fainted. And how deep is the faint of the Messenger of God! (*One of the men, al-Mugaira, looks at the face of the Prophet.*)

AL-MUGAIRA: Oh Omar, . . . By God! The Messenger of God is dead!

OMAR (*furiously*): Liar! The Messenger of God has not died. . . . but you . . . you're a man whom deception has trapped! The Messenger of God shall not die until the hypocrites are destroyed. (*Abbas looks at the face of the Prophet but does not answer; then Omar, Abbas, and the men leave.*)

THE PEOPLE (*off stage*): Is the Prophet dead. . . . Has the Prophet died?

OMAR (*shouting off stage*): Oh, you people . . . I don't want to hear anyone say that Mohammed has died. But he has only been summoned—just as Moses the son of Imran was summoned when he stayed apart from his people for 40 nights. And, by God, I hope that any man who says that Mohammed has died will have his hands and feet cut off!

THE PEOPLE (*off stage*): Do not bury him. . . . He has not died!

A MAN (*off stage*): Verily the Messenger of God has been

raised—just as Jesus the son of Mary arose, and he shall
return! °

ABBAS (*off stage*): Does anyone from among you have a statement from the Messenger of God about his death? If so,
then tell us.

THE PEOPLE (*off stage*): No! We have no such statement.

ABBAS (*off stage*): And do you, Omar, have anything such as
that?

OMAR (*off stage*): No!

ABBAS (*off stage*): Witness then all of you that only a liar can
now say that he has any sort of statement about his death
after Mohammed's death. And by God!—who is None but
the One God—the Prophet has surely tasted death, and his
body will surely decay, just as have those of all men. So
bury your companion. Does God put one of you to death
only once and put *him* to death twice? He is more precious
to God than that. He did not die until he had made the
"way" clear and manifest, had allowed the lawful and outlawed the forbidden, had married and divorced, made war
and peace. . . . And no shepherd conducting his sheep to
the mountain tops was more enduring or persevering than
was the Messenger of God on your behalf.

THE WOMEN (*behind the curtain*): Did the Messenger of God
die or has he not died?

FATIMA (*comes out, draws near the body, and contemplates
the face of the Prophet for a long time; then bursts out
crying*): The Messenger of God has died.

ABU BAKR (*enters and rushes up to the body, raises the shroud
from the still Prophet, and kisses him crying*): Would that
I could exchange my father or mother for you. Blessed are
you alive and dead. As for the death which God decreed for
you, you have tasted it. Now never again can a death strike
you down. (*He returns the cloak over the face of the
Prophet and leaves.*)

OMAR (*off stage*): Oh, you people! By God, the Messenger

° According to the Koran (sura IV, verse 157-8) Jesus was not
crucified or killed, but was "taken up" alive by God.

of God is *not* dead. His soul has only ascended just as the soul of Moses ascended . . . !

ABU BAKR *(off stage)*: Calm down, Omar, and listen!

OMAR *(continuing)*: And by God, the Messenger of God will never die until certain people lose their hands and tongues!

ABU BAKR *(off stage, calling out loudly)*: Oh, People . . . *(He reads from the Koran)* "Mohammed is but a messenger, messengers the like of whom have passed away before him. Will it be that when he dieth or is slain, ye will turn back on your heels? He who turneth back doth no hurt to Allah, but Allah will reward the thankful." And whosoever of you worships Mohammed, know that Mohammed is dead, but he who worships God, know that God is ever living and cannot die.

THE PEOPLE *(off stage)*: The Prophet of God is dead!

AKKAYYA

RAJA RAO

I, nor do I think any of my cousins, never knew what she was actually called. Everybody in the family called her Akkayya, elder sister, and we simply followed the example of our parents and aunts. I have, nevertheless, a faint remembrance that when they were talking to the Brahmins about the obsequies, they called her Venkatalakshamma, Subbamma or Nanjamma, one of those old names which meant all that a virtuous woman ought to have, that is, *virtue*.

My first vivid impressions of Akkayya go back to my childhood. I must have been about four; and having just lost my mother, I was left under her care, till my father married again and started his new family. I used to be very devoted to Akkayya, and had a strange, instinctive pity for her. She must have been over sixty, and I always saw her with the same childlike smile, with eyes that moved like the marbles I played with, and her face all wrinkled like a dry mango, more wrinkled than ever when she smiled. When the summer sun abruptly disappeared and a starry night spread above us, I used to be seated on her lap, in the verandah of the Fig-Tree House. The evening I remember so well, she sat looking toward the town, where the lights were being lit in houses and in shops; and all of a sudden she turned toward me and kissed me. She spoke very little, but when she did she lisped like a child.

"Ta-ta-ta, Ma-mama," she whispered to me, "Tatatta, ma-mamma, you are a sweet angel."

"Kaka-ka, Gaga-ga," I imitated, and turning round slipped my hands under her ochre sari and squeezed her hanging breasts in childish joy. She felt happy and never once did she scold me for it, except, as I observed later, when I did it before everybody.

"You are a little darling," she said and kissed me again, pressing me to her breasts.

"You are a darling too!" I rolled over in her lap.

"Now! There! Come and sit here!" she commanded, and I obeyed her. Sitting on her lap I was pained that she did not talk to me any more. And I sat thinking of the little calf that had died the day before, and the snake that I had seen that morning. Again she suddenly turned toward me and kissed me, almost violently.

"Akkayya, Akkayya!" I cried happily.

"My child, my darling!" she murmured and kissed me again. Not knowing how to show her my affection, I put my hand upon her shaven head and caressed it, though it was rough and prickly. She seemed uneasy and, pulling up her sari-fringe over her head, she took off my hand and held it in hers, tenderly. I was hurt and sad.

"Akkayya!" I called suddenly, "Akkayya, why is your head shaven, when all others like aunt Nagamma and aunt Kenchamma and aunt Ranganayaki have their long, long hair?" It was dark and I could not see her face, but the silence that followed was heavy and sad.

"Why, Akkayya?" I repeated.

"Because I am a widow, my child," she answered, dry as the shopkeeper I bought gram from.

"A widow? What is it, Akkayya?" I squeezed her breasts again, in affection.

"A widow is a widow, my child." She was surely sad.

"You are like aunt Nagamma and aunt Kenchamma, and

you say you are a widow? No. You are one like us!" I explained.

"No, my child. Nagamma and Kenchamma have husbands. I have none."

"Oh! no. You surely have, Akkayya. You have."

"I haven't, my son. I haven't! . . ." She was embarrassed and sad. Her hands trembled.

"Nagamma has uncle Shama, Kenchamma has uncle Subbu, cousin Sita has grandpa, and you . . . and you . . . have me," I muttered with a shrill mischievous laugh. It relieved her. She pressed me again to her breasts and kissed me.

"You naughty little imp!" she cried, comforted.

She had to go to the kitchen and I sat there thinking over the things I had done and I wanted to do. The next morning the cows were being driven to the fields by Mada, and I would follow him. I would see how they grazed. Then, coming back, I would offer rice to the sparrows, when my grandfather sat reading big, big books to the neighbors. Then again, young Sundra would come to play marbles with me like today. How I would enjoy it! To play marbles . . . Akkayya came back silent as ever and sitting down took me into her lap. She looked troubled, nervous. Uncle Shama came in followed by the peasants and my grandfather was howling inside against somebody. In that confusion, we were strangely near each other and we felt one. I knew when she kissed me more, she loved me more, and when I squeezed her breasts more, I loved her more. . . .

"Why are you sad, Akkayya?" I asked, whispering with fear.

"Oh! . . . nothing," she answered, dull and disgusted.

"And you do not put on holy vermilion either," I said, trying to find out what a widow meant. At that moment, apart from men, I had only known there were giants called "thieves." A widow! It must be something like that. But still. . . . No. I knew Akkayya so well. After a moment she answered me in the same sad tone.

"My child, I am a widow. . . ."

"But, Akkayya," I insisted, "it cannot be. You go to the

temple like them, you *are* like them. . . . Why, Akkayya?"

"I am a widow," she cried out in anger and loked towards the stars. I trembled and sat silent. Her hands touched mine. And I remembered that they were bare, bare like a tree. Aunt Nagamma and aunt Kenchamma wore bangles that clinked and sang. And she had none. And she always wore the same dull sari; not the blue, beautiful, gold-bordered ones of my aunts. Was she different from them? Was she? They had children too, Ganga and Parvathi and Swami, and Leela and Susheela with whom I played. Whenever they fell down or were hurt in a game, they went back weeping like dogs to their mothers, full of such false complaints. I hated them. I only loved Akkayya. And she? No children?

"Where are your children, Akkayya?" I asked, sheltering myself under her breasts.

"I have none," she answered angrily.

"And I?" I managed to say.

"You. . . . You are Ranga's son, not mine." She breathed hard.

"Why have you no children, Akkayya?" I asked again.

"Because, because I have no husband," she answered indifferently.

"What is a husband, Akkayya?"

"Oh, be quiet! and don't bother me with all your *Ramayana*. A husband is a husband, a man. . . ."

"Am I a man, Akkayya?"

"I don't know!" she wailed. I was silent again. I had been half-initiated into the secrets of a "widow" and I would not leave it at that. I wanted to know more: I had to know more. A man, a man, I repeated to myself. Uncle Shama was a man. Uncle Subbu was a man. Yes! They were. They dressed in dhotis. They were not like aunt Kenchamma and aunt Nagamma.

"But why have you not a man, Akkayya? Kenchamma has one, Nagamma has one. . . ."

"Oh! Be still, you pariah, or I'll sew up your lips."

I kept quiet and sat still. In a moment my father called me to go and have my dinner, and I sat amongst my aunts and uncles and my cousins as quiet as a cat. I was thinking: so widows don't have children either. No. Why not? I looked round and saw my uncles and my aunts and my cousins. Aunt Nagamma had uncle Shama; aunt Kenchamma had uncle Subbu; aunt Nagamma and uncle Shama had Susheela and Swami sitting beside them; aunt Kenchamma and uncle Subbu had Ganga and Parvathi and Leela, who sat by them. And Akkayya? . . . I ought to have sat by her. Suppose I asked her why she never ate with us? "Widow!" again. "Hush, you monkey!" in her anger. No.

The dinner over I went to the central hall where Akkayya had already spread her bedding and laid herself down. She called me affectionately, and asking me whether I had eaten well and what I had eaten, she kissed me and asked me to get into the bed. I was so happy to find her gentle that I forgot all about my researches into the mystery of "widowhood" and hardly in bed I slept like a prince.

After my father's wife had gone to live with him and had started the new household, I had naturally to go back. Of course I wept and shrieked when they were taking me away from Akkayya. But they gave me a big piece of yellow sugar-candy and put me into a horse cart, and I forgot about everything, and not until I had arrived at my father's did I discover that Akkayya was no more with me. Well, I did not weep very much, for my father gave me semolina sweets and a blue filigree cap and my step-mother was as sweet as one could be. She not only played with me and put round my neck a gold chain with a shining diamond star, but . . . but, if you do not tell anyone I will whisper in your ears that she even suckled me as though I were but a tiny little baby.

During holidays we often went back to Talassana, but never again had I the same affection for Akkayya. My aunt Ranganayaki having died, her two children were left under Akkayya's care and she seemed just as contented with them as she had been with me. Only once, I remember, she was particularly affectionate towards me and gave me a pair of gold bangles. I was so happy with the present that I kissed her as before. But, being grown up now, I could not bear the smell of her mouth and I never did it again.

During one of these holiday visits to my grandfather—I was about ten or eleven years old then—it struck me that I should know more about Akkayya. I wanted to ask somebody, but going to one of my aunts or cousins I would be so overcome with fear that I would excuse myself and run away, awkwardly. At last one day I got a very good chance. Uncle Shama loved me and he often called me to go and lie by him. That evening aunt Nagamma was busy in the kitchen, and being alone I took courage to ask who Akkayya was and why she lived with us. The words uncle Shama used I cannot quite remember, but it was something like what I am going to relate to you.

She was a sister of my grandmother, and was the eldest of eight children, three girls and five boys. Her parents were very rich people and my great-grandfather had even been a Minister once. That was, as you must remember, over a hundred years ago. Akkayya was a pretty little girl, full of charm and intelligence. When she was five she had already begun to discuss the holy scriptures with her father, and her horoscope foretold a most brilliant marriage. Her father, when a Minister, had known the Ministers of many neighboring states. I do not know if you have ever heard of the Gagana State, on the banks of the Cauvery, just where it falls down the precipice into the frothy chasm below. Gagana was a small state but it had a good king and his Minister, Ramakrishnayya, was an intelligent and able administrator. Ramakrishnayya had often come and stayed with Akkayya's father, that is my great-grandfather, and having lately lost his second wife, he was intending to marry again. When Akkayya's father heard of it he straightway sent a Brahmin to negotiate for his daughter's marriage. Ramakrishnayya had never expected to be able to marry the daughter of an ex-Minister of Mysore State; and he was so flattered with the proposal that he came running and accepted the hand of Akkayya with becoming humility and grace. Akkayya must have been about eight or nine years of age then, but Ramakrishnayya was already a grandfather. The whole of Mysore was invited for the marriage week, and if uncle Shama is to be believed—he had, I must say, a very rich imagination—the Maharaja himself came to grace the occasion. The marriage over, the bridegroom's party left for Gagana, amidst hymns and holy music, leaving the little wife to come of age. Not very long after, Akkayya's father received a letter to say that Ramakrishnayya had died of "some fever," and they wept and they moaned for a few days, and after that everything went on as usual. Akkayya did not understand anything of it; she was absorbed in the doll show—for it was Dassera then. They only asked her not to put the vermilion mark on her brow and she did not mind that in the very least.

Years passed. Akkayya came of age, and as was meet for a widow, she was shaven and sent to her husband's family in Gagana where she was received with due respect and affection. Her stepson, now about forty-five years of age, treated her as one of his own daughters, some of whom were married and had children of their own. Akkayya soon became the mistress of the kitchen—she was the only widow there—and she did the cleaning of the vessels and the sweeping of the floors, as though she were born with a vessel at her waist and a broom in her hand. For four or five years she lived on thus and she was more than happy in that "full house"; there were always children to play with, girls to talk to, cows to milk, and the temple to go to—oh, such an easy, quiet life. Her daughter-in-law, that is her step-son's wife, was a good woman, and as she was three months in the year in confinement, three other months in pregnancy, and nearly half the rest of the time in bed due to a fever or a cough, she did not bother Akkayya at all, and everything was perfect. When Akkayya went to the temple everybody stepped aside saying, "The Minister's wife" . . . "The Minister's wife," and she felt so proud of being thus addressed that she went there more than ever before.

Akkaya herself had told me a story, which I had completely forgotten and would never have remembered had not uncle Shama referred to it again. One day she wanted to see the waterfall. She had heard the *bhus-bhus* of it all the time but had never once gone anywhere near it. So a trip was duly arranged, and one of the police officers led the family of the Minister to the place where the Cauvery gallops forth into the narrow gorge, gurgling and swishing and rising majestically into the air like a seven-headed cobra. What do you think Akkayya saw? Would you believe me, she actually saw with those very eyes she had—and they were sharp I assure you—she actually saw miles and miles of thick, strong jute rope swallowed by the chasm . . . and God only knew how much deeper it was. They told the Minister's family that the abyss communicated with the center of the earth. Oh, how wonderful!

Akkayya was now about eighteen. She always loved children and she began to ask why she could not have any. Uncle Shama added his own opinion by saying—and I hardly understood it then—that above all women want children and the childless are jealous of all mothers. Whatever it was, Akkayya began to quarrel with her step-granddaughter and in a year things had grown so impossible that her stepson wrote to her brothers, my great-grandfather was dead by that time, to take her away, which they soon did. But it is a pity that her stepson should have been so mean as to say that she wanted to poison one of his daughters or that she wanted to sleep with him. I assure you, Akkayya was as pure a thing as the jasmine in the temple garden. When people hate others they always mix milk and salt. . . . Anyway Akkayya was back in her family and everybody was happy about it.

But that could not go on very long either, as her brothers did not agree between themselves and they quarreled so much with one another that the family had to break up, the five brothers taking their own share of the patrimony. But nobody wanted to take Akkayya for even here she had begun to be jealous of her sisters-in-law, all of whom had many children. So, my grandmother asked her to come and stay with her in Talassana, and for fifty years or more she lived in our family without quarrels or complaints. My grandmother

was a sharp woman—God give her peace in her next life!—
and she knew how to treat people. She let Akkayya have all
the children to herself and Akkayya was as happy as a deer.
She cooked for the family, sometimes discussed philosophy
with my grandfather, and during the rest of the time she
played with us. And, especially when by some strange misfortune three of my aunts successively died, leaving three,
eight and five children, she had always enough children to
take care of, and she treated them all alike, kind when they
were good and severe when they were mischivous. And
when these children left her, she forgot them as the cow forgets her young ones. But God always supplied her with or-
phan children, and as you will soon see it was these who
stood around her as she breathed her last. That was her
karma!

When uncle Shama told me the story I could not help
weeping. And thinking of Akkayya I had a sudden vision of
the black, moss-grown rock that hung over the Nandi precipice, firm, but insecure; it would fall now or it would never;
and when the winds would rise and the tempests toss it over
into the great mouth below, it would be no more, no more
and all its hardships spent and lost. . . . The sky was gathering clouds.

I do not know why, but we did not go back to Talassana
for four or five years. And the only news we had was a card
that my grandmother sent us every three or four months to
say everybody was well and that they were "hoping to hear
from us that all the prosperity, health and the hundred and
eight joys" were given to us "by the benevolent gods." Only
once, I think, however, was there a line about Akkayya being
ill and that she had been bedridden for the past year. One
year! It was never to be taken literally. Women have such
a strong imagination! My father said he was sorry that
Akkayya, who had never known sickness in her life, should
now be in bed; and saying to ourselves that she would soon
be better we never talked of it again. My grandmother did
not say a word about it in the next two cards, and not until

cousin Ramu returned after his short visit to Talassana did we hear the full story.

One day after finishing her bath, Akkayya went and sat by the tulsi plant to say her prayers. She caught a bad cold and that very night it developed into a high fever. My grandmother, naturally, gave her some decoctions of herbs—a family secret she had known all her life. But the next day the fever was still as high, and my grandmother gave her the same medicine. It was only on the third day, when Akkayya was almost unconscious, that they thought of calling a doctor. But she hated doctors—hated them like pariahs. To drink a medicine prepared with the hands of those wretches— those irreligious, low-born, dissolute blackguards! No. No. She would rather die. They tried to persuade her; then they threatened her. But it was all in vain. That evening their neighbor Venkatappa's wife came to see her and brought a new decoction for "such a fever"—also an old wives' secret. It did not do any good either, and on the fifth day the doctor was actually sent for without Akkayya's knowledge. As soon as she saw him she rose up and, sitting in her bed, scowled and spat on him, so angry she was. But the doctor was accustomed to such welcomes. He asked my grandmother and grandfather to hold her two hands, and in spite of her howlings and moanings, he examined her and declared it to be a serious case of typhoid. He told them to be very careful, keep her warm, give her light food, and gave them a prescription to be filled at the Civil Hospital. My grandfather and grandmother did not know how to proceed, as Akkayya would never drink medicine brought from the hospital. They sat together and discussed it, and as my grandmother was a clever woman she suggested it could easily be mixed with coffee or soup; and so the medicine was brought. When Akkayya said, "Sister, this soup smells horrible!" my grandmother would explain that when people have fever "everything has a strange taste," and Akkayya never discovered the trick. But the medicine did not work, for Akkayya always wanted delicious mango pickles to "clear her mouth," as she used to say.

Besides she kept talking all the time in her weak, delirious state.

It was a forty-eight-days' fever and when it left her she was nothing but bone and eyes. For two months or more she could not get up, and when she even sat for a moment she complained that her bones ached. At last she decided she would get up for the Shivaratri, and every day she used to tell herself that she was going to be better, and how wonderful it would be to stand up and walk. Sleeping in her bed, she used to dream of the day she would have a good bath by the well, say her prayers, adorn the idols and keep awake all the night listening to the miracles of Shiva, the three-eyed one. In her joy she even sang in her hoarse, breathless voice:

> Shiva is Sri Rama,
> Shiva is the Lord of the all-dowered Gauri,
> Shiva is Sri Vishnu,
> Shiva is the King of the Crematorium,
> Shiva is Ganges-crowned,
> Shiva is snake-garlanded,
> Shiva is poison-throated,
> Shiva is the All, the All,
> Shiva is Sri Rama,
> Shiva is the Lord of the all-dowered Gauri.

My grandmother, who heard it from the kitchen, was happy too and prayed that her sister would soon be able to live as usual. Only, when Shivaratri came, they tried to lift her up and make her stand, but her legs had lost all their strength and they bent down like plantain bark. They tried to make her stand by giving her their shoulders to lean on, by giving her two boxes to rest her hands upon; even by leaving her beside the pillars, but nothing would work. Akkayya was smiling all the while. She felt happy like a child that stands up for the first time, and she persuaded herself that she would be able to go to the temple by the evening—though for the moment the experiment was not so great a success! Anyway, at ten the barber came and shaved her. Then they took her into the bathroom—they actually carried her—and she sat on the bath slab smiling and joking. She would get better. Of course, she would! After the bath they carried her to the sanctum and, leaning against the wall, she prayed as usual, her little silver pot by her and the rosary in her hand. Then they wanted her to go to bed, but she refused and insisted on eating with all the others. But in the middle of the meal, when she was just going to eat rice and curds, she fell down and rolled across her food. They washed her and took her back to bed and it was over a quarter of an hour before she recovered her consciousness. She did not seem sad. Her eyes still glowed with the ecstacy of a child, and she lay in the bed, smiling.

Of course she could not go to the temple that night. But she would soon—by Sankranthi. After one year, she still lay in her bed, much to weak even to sit up. But how very gay she was! Here, cousin Ramu who told us the story, suddenly lowered his voice and began to whisper as though he were going to tell us a secret. We were anxious and listened with all our ears. "The truth is," he murmured, "the truth is, I think she has a bad disease. . . ." Bad disease! I did not know what it meant. Nor do I know now. I only saw that my father's face turned grey as a coconut and my stepmother shivered. "She stinks, she stinks horribly . . ." whispered cousin Ramu with disgust. "She stinks like a manure pit. I could not sit by her. I could not stay there for more than five minutes. . . . And yet," he said as though consoled, "you never saw her smile like that. She has the smile of a godly child. . . ."

That night I had a most horrible nightmare.

It was a cold morning. My bedding in hand, I walked from the station to the Old-Well House where my grandmother now lived. (My grandfather had lately died and uncle Shama, who loved his independence, stayed in the Fig-Tree House and sent Akkayya and my grandmother to the other one.) As I entered the courtyard my grandmother hailed me from the verandah where she was sweeping the floor. It was not a very big house. Just three rooms and a kitchen, with a spacious, elevated verandah, and a large courtyard with a sweet-water well in the middle. As I neared the house every step seemed to drag back and every breath sniff and choke at the thought of Akkayya. I looked at the doors. They seemed so gruesome and bare. In which room was she? In which?

My grandmother whispered to me.

"The children are asleep," she said.

"Which children?" I inquired.

"Why! Sata's . . . Sata's . . ." she answered, a little hurt.

"But. . . . You mean they're all here?"

"No, no," she whispered, beckoning me to sit on the parapet wall, "only the last two are here. The father kept the eldest son and the eldest daughter with him."

"When did they come here?" I asked.

"Over a month ago. Soon after Sata's death. . . ." It made me sad to think of aunt Sata. She was the dearest of women; she had died in childbirth.

"How is *she*?" I managed to say, trembling.

"Who?"

"She. . . ." I pointed toward one of the doors that seemed, I cannot say why, to be Akkayya's room.

"You mean Akkayya?" she asked pained.

"Yes!"

"Well!" Here my grandmother had tears in her eyes. "Well, son, she is between life and death. I wish she would die soon." It sent a shiver through my back. For a brief moment we did not say a word to each other.

"Anyhow," she began, trying to change the subject, "tell me, how is everybody at home. Your father? Your sisters?"

"They're all well," I said casually. My eyes were strangely drawn towards that door—Akkayya's door. Was she there?

In the meanwhile the milk-woman came and my grandmother went into the kitchen to get a vessel. I looked around. The morning was breaking. The sun was spreading his feathers like an amorous peacock. But it was still very cold. And somehow even the mango tree I loved so much was sad and sickly. The bullock carts were creaking along, and the dust of the morning was rising. I was not going to stay with my grandmother. I had decided to go to my uncle's and had dropped in here only to pay my respects to her and to inquire after Akkayya. Now I must be going. . . . Somehow I felt breathless and worm-eaten. Even my grandmother's face, which was always lively and young, looked as though she were being strangled. No, I must be going. But my grandmother insisted that I should stay and have a cup of coffee. I could not refuse it. But I could not stay there any longer. Telling my grandmother I would go and wash my face at the well, I walked out into the courtyard. The raw air, the pomegranates and the sky above seemed to give the sense of a fresher reality. I sat on the wall of the well, thinking of my grandfather, aunt Sata, Akkayya, and all those whom I had loved and lived with, and who were slowly disappearing one by one.

The children came out. Naga was a little girl of nine, pale, anemic and quiet. Ramu was about four, plump, wild and mischievous. I tried to talk to them and told them I was their cousin. But that did not seem to interest them. "One more of us," they seemed to say and walked away to wash their faces. Even in their countenance there was something heavy, sad, decaying. Death had entered the house like a cobra. When would He leave it?

The coffee was ready. Naga came to call me. I had not yet washed and so I simply threw a little water on my face, dried it and went in. Nobody was to speak loudly. Everything was hushed and uneasy.

"Do you want to see *her?*" my grandmother asked. I felt as though I were going to vomit.

"No," I said, nodding my head uncomfortably.

"She calls you a thousand times a day, and says she will not die without seeing you. . . ." My grandmother was in tears. I coughed.

"She wants badly to see you, my child. She says everybody in Talassana hates her, only you, your father and your mother ever cared for her. . . . Oh, to see her weep! She weeps like a mad woman. And when she shrieks the tiles seem to fly to the skies! Suppose you see her?"

"No. I do not want to bother her." I lied.

"It's no bother. She would weep to see you. My child, you must!"

"Yes, it is true," added Naga. "She always calls you and tells us you were born like a prince and you would be one. She tells us so many stories about you." She laughed, and hid her face between her knees.

"No," I said, "I will not see her now. As I will stay in town for another two or three days—we shall see." My grandmother understood me and didn't insist any more.

"My child," she exclaimed, sorrowful and breathless, "my life here is really dreadful. Oh! to be living thus. . . ." She wept. "These children are already a burden, and in addition Akkayya. . . . No. Not a moment to breathe and not a moment to call my own. And then—" Here I heard from a neighboring room Akkayya's shrieking voice.

"Naga! Naga! You dirty widow, you daughter of a prostitute, you donkey-whore! Come, or I'll flay you alive!"

Naga squirmed in her place. Her day was beginning. I must confess it sent a chill through me as though rising from a rotting well.

"Naga! Naga! hé, hé Naga! you dirty donkey-whore!"

My grandmother nodded her head and asked Naga to answer.

"You see, my child, that is how it is twenty-four hours in the day. I do not know where she learnt these filthy words of abuse, but not even a pariah would use them before his wife, such are her curses. "Naga, Naga." Always "Naga." This poor child, beaten and skinned to her last bone by her father, has come to live here, and her life as you see is worse than a dog's life. She has to take food to her, put it into her mouth, clean her bed, sweep the floor, and for absolution sit listening to her mad, mad stories. But you see, my child," continued my grandmother, trying to be a little kinder to her sister, "you see, sometimes she folds these two children in her arms and weeps over them for their unhappiness. She calls them by all sorts of endearing names—my parrot, my calf, my diamond. . . ."

"That's true! She is sometimes very good," agreed Naga.

"Naga, you concubine, Naga, you wretch, Naga, you donkey
. . ." recommenced Akkayya. There was a painful silence for
a moment. We all stopped breathing. Naga sipped at her
coffee.

"Does she ever get up?" I ventured.

"Never. We carry her to the bath and bring her back. All
the morning I do nothing but wash her dirty clothes, we
have two beds for her which we change each day. We wash
her saris, take her to the bath, wash her, take her back and
we put her in her new bed." Here she seemed to draw back
her hands and wipe them with her sari to feel sure the foul
smell was not sticking to them. "She is never silent even for
a moment, and we can never have anybody here or go to see
anybody."

"But," I said, "why not?"

"Why? The moment she hears me going down the steps
she begins to shriek for me and weep and roll in her bed
till I go to her. And when I go she asks me to sit, and when
I sit, she laughs at me and tells me a story I have heard a
million times before."

"You see, son, that is my life. At my age—I am sixty-two
now—I cannot even go on a pilgrimage and lead a pious
life. Nothing but curses in my ears, instead of Ram Ram, and
nothing but washing filth the whole day instead of sacred
baths in the Ganges and the Jumna. . . ." She began to sob.
What could I do? Again it started:

"Naga, you wretch, Naga, Naga . . . Naga. I will burn you
today if you do not come," Akkayya shrieked.

"Go, Naga, go," said my grandmother, and the little girl
limped out of the room mechanically.

"Listen! Listen and hear what she will tell her." I went
nearer the wall.

"You dirty whore, you dog-born, you donkey's wife, this is
how you come when I call you! I have been shouting for
you for hours. Oh, I wish I could get up and tear your skin
like my sari. You dirty donkey-whore! Why don't you all let
me die? Leave me, throw me into the well and drink a good,

hot ser of milk? You would, wouldn't you? You cur, dirty cur. Why don't you go and sleep with the servant, you concubine?"

"Tell me, what do you want?" said Naga. Her voice was firm and indifferent.

"What do I want? What do I want? I want some coffee to drink, some hot water to wash with. And you are a dear, a darling. Come and kiss me."

Naga came back and sat with us as though nothing had happened. Hardly had she sipped her coffee than Akkayya again called out:

"Naga . . . Naaga. . . . N-a-aga." She moaned like a dying woman. "Go," said my grandmother. Naga went, the cup of coffee in her hand.

"Now tell me, donkey-whore, who is it that has been here this morning? Sister has been talking to him all the time."

"Nobody. It is only your dream," answered Naga drily.

"You buffalo! You concubine! Don't tell me a lie."

Naga came back and Akkayya continued to shriek. My grandmother rose up in a fury and went out with a thousand curses upon her lips. I put my ear to the wall and listened.

"So you have come back, dear sister, dear sister," said Akkayya with such love that my grandmother was suddenly disarmed.

"Why did you come, dear sister?"

"Because you shrieked."

"Did I? But tell me, dear sister, when will you burn me?"

"Don't speak nonsense," consoled my grandmother, troubled.

"Nonsense. No. Tell me only one thing: When I am dead and when you have burnt me, will you ever remember me?" She laughed.

"Why do you speak such queer words, Akkayya?" my grandmother asked comfortingly.

"No, sister, no. I have given you so much trouble, such sinner's trouble. Will you always remember me, me you elder sister?"

"Surely! And respect you as ever. . . ." From my grandmother's voice I knew she had melted into tears.

"When I am dead, sister," continued Akkayya, "be sure to write to Nanjunda, Ramanna and Mari, and tell them their sister died with their names upon her lips." She too seemed to weep. "Tell them, I am their elder sister—and though they never once did give me as much as a sari, tell them, I love them all. . . ."

"Amma, amma," wept my grandmother and—God knows what made her say that—she whispered, "Akkayya, little Kittu is here. . . ."

"Kittu . . . Kittu . . . My darling Kittu . . . My son, my child, Kittu!" she cried madly. I trembled and gasped for breath. Would I go? Would I? But her words rang in my ears like bells of the temple. "Kittu . . . Kittu . . . My son, come, come!" Unconsciously I was up and was walking toward Akkayya's room. The two children followed me. Even at the door a foul stench enveloped me. I entered.

Akkayya lay there, her eyes white, her face pouchy and husklike, and she looked at me—a true image of death. Then suddenly she turned towards the wall and cried out: "Kittu . . . Kittu . . . Kittu . . ." like a frightened animal.

Naga bent down and covered her parched thighs . . . And I wept.

One evening when I came home—some four years later—everybody looked annoyed and uneasy. I wondered what it was. They asked me to remove my outer garments and go into the hall. I knew somebody had died. My sister? Uncle Shama? Cousin Susheela? Who? Who? I went into the hall, trembling. My stepmother had already bathed beneath the tap, and the water was being boiled in the bathroom for all of us.

"Akkayya is dead," said my father irritably and in utter disgust.

"When?" I gasped.

"The day before yesterday," said my stepmother. I sat like

all of them, waiting to have my bath; but I assure you my soul was in true distress. "Akkayya . . . Akkayya . . ." I said to myself like one who calls a beloved soul, "Akkayya. . . ." I heard my stepmother say:

"Could they not have had the sense to hide it from us for *the* six months? What a nuisance!"

"Idiots!" howled my father.

"Perfect idiots," spat my stepmother.

"Who is Akkayya?" asked my little sister.

"A great aunt whom you have never seen, and thank heavens will never see," said my stepmother and walked away into the kitchen.

We duly bathed, changed our clothing, and after dinner we went to the cinema.

I think, between the three brothers of my grandmother, my father, and a cousin of ours, none of them wanted to take the responsibility of performing Akkayya's obsequies. At last one of her brothers called a Brahmin, and giving him a few rupees, asked him to perform the "necessary" ceremonies. I do not know whether the Brahmin did it. Anyway, here I have written the story of Akkayya, maybe her only funeral ceremony.

Notes on Contributors

AHMED ALI is a member of the Pakistani Foreign Service Secretariat. His *Twilight in Delhi* was published in London in 1940. • ERIC BENTLEY, drama critic, director, and author, is Brander Matthews Professor of Dramatic Literature at Columbia. • BERTOLT BRECHT, a potent voice in world drama since his *Three Penny Opera* in 1922, left Germany in 1933, is now back in Berlin. • Just as he was beginning to be recognized in France, young RENÉ-GUY CADOU died, in 1951. His work shows the influence of Rimbaud, Apollinaire, and Breton. • FRANCIS CARCO, prolific French poet and novelist, frequents the bistros of the *métier* and is a member of the Académie Goncourt. • R. V. CASSILL has had short stories published in *The Best American Short Stories,* as well as two novels, *Eagle on the Cover* and *Dormitory Women.* • KAY CICELLIS was born in Marseilles of Greek parents. Grove Press published her novel, *No Name in the Streets.* • FAZIL DAGLARCA has published several volumes of poetry in Turkish and is considered one of the leading poets of the Middle East. • EDWARD DAHLBERG, who has been called by Sir Herbert Read "perhaps the greatest prose writer of our time," lives in California. • OSAMU DAZAI (1909–1948) reached his full stature only after the war, with semi-autobiographical works such as "Villon's Wife." • RENÉ DAUMAL is one of the most important of France's post-surrealist poets (1908–1944). • ROBERT DESNOS, French poet and jazz authority, died in a concentration camp. • SAMI FERLIOL graduated last year from teachers' training Capa Institute at Istanbul. • HERBERT GOLD, author of two distinguished novels, is on the staff of Wayne University. • TAWFIQ AL-HAKIM, Egypt's ranking writer, has successfully edited out of the extensive *Traditions* a life of Mohammed. • H. R. HAYS, novelist and poet, translated and edited *Twelve Spanish American Poets*, and has written TV plays. • The pastoralism, imagism, acceptance of life, and *Schwärmerei* of FRANCIS JAMMES (1868–1937) make him one of France's most influential modern poets. • JACK JONES has lived mostly in New York, where for the past six years he has worked in factories. • DONALD KEENE, born in New York, 1922, graduated from Columbia, studied at Harvard, and was lecturer in Japanese at Cambridge University. • SIEGFRIED LAUTERWASSER is a professional photographer for industry and tourist agencies. • MICHEL LEIRIS (1901–   ) is one of France's most important post-surrealist poets. • MARGARITA LYBERAKI, writer and painter, was born in Athens in 1920. Her novel *Trois Étés* won the prize for the year's best foreign work translated and published in France. • FEDERICO GARCIA LORCA (1898–1936), Spain's great modern poet and dramatist, visted New York in 1929. • OSCAR VENCELAS LUBICSMILOSZ (1877–1939) spent his adult years in Paris and wrote in French. His poetry is much in vogue today. • BEAUMONT NEWHALL, curator of the Eastman Museum, is the author of *The History of Photography from 1839 to the Present Day*. • A. TURAN OFLAZOGLU is a student at the University of Istanbul. • ENRICO PEA (1881–   ), Italian novelist, poet, playwright, and short-story writer, here makes what is possibly his first appearance in English, translated by EZRA POUND, who as a translator has made whole literatures new and immediate to English readers. *Moscardino* is the only novel he has ever been tempted to translate. • WILLIAM R. POLK (1929–   ), Rockefeller Fellow, author of *What the Arabs Think*, studied in Latin America and the Middle East. • RAJA RAO, novelist and philosopher from South India, has lived mostly in France and England. • PIERRE REVERDY's reputation has risen steadily in recent years as one of the best of the "cubist generation" of poets. • KENNETH REXROTH is a poet, abstract painter, critic, and translator. His *One Hundred Japanese Poems* will appear this fall. • E. N. SARGENT has been published by the *Atlantic* and *Harper's*. • After teaching English and French in Germany, GEORGETTE R. SCHULER has taught modern European languages at Wells and Washington State colleges. • KHUSHWANT SINGH, a Sikh, now with UNESCO, is winner of the Grove Press Prize for his *Mano Majra*, soon to be issued. • AARON SISKIND is instructor in photography at the Institute of Design, Chicago. • CÉSAR VALLEJO, Peru's greatest modern poet, attended the University of Trujillo, then in 1923 went to Paris, where he died in poverty in 1938. • PETER WEISS, exponent of Swedish existentialism, is both painter and writer. • BRETT WESTON, photographer, was a Guggenheim Fellow in 1945. • MINOR WHITE, creative photographer, teacher, and writer, is editor and publisher of *Aperture*. • (Madame) GUZIN YALTER is on the staff of the Library at the American Information Center in Istanbul.